LOT'S WIFE

Monique Bosco

LOT'S WIFE

Translated from the French by
John Glassco

McClelland and Stewart Limited

The Canadian Publishers
McClelland and Stewart Limited
25 Hollinger Road, Toronto

The publishers wish to acknowledge the support of the
Canada Council for the translation of this book.

Printed and bound in Canada
by
John Deyell Company

TO SHEILA FISCHMAN
THIS TRANSLATION

1

I'm looking at my window. Thinking, *one jump, and I escape the horrible sound of this voice.* This gentle voice suddenly become the voice of an enemy. No one has ever tortured me like this. . . . But in this country of snow and ice the windows don't open. I can't escape.

The suddenness of it all doubles my stupor. Yesterday I suspected nothing. And here I am, *deceased.* The I of yesterday is dead. Only a little while ago she fancied her life hung on your gaze.

My head, empty; my body, useless. This body suddenly rejected, pushed aside. What shall I do with it? Where shall I throw it, how get rid of it? No, I must listen, and try to understand the sentence you're passing on me.

"I'm glad to see you're behaving reasonably."

So I appear reasonable, at this moment I've always dreaded. Well, you're a doctor; you ought to recognize all the symptoms of a loss of reason.

You're used to passing terrible sentences on people. Your technique is remarkable. First, deliver the blow: *the illness may be fatal.* Then announce the remedy: *amputation.* The solution is hailed with positive joy.

Those condemned to an imminent death are equally "reasonable." As a reward, the pretty joys of the invalid are danced before them.

So now you've taken the plunge. You breathe more easily. At last you stop talking. Now you've risen, and in the most comfortable, most physicianly tone you assure me of your readiness to serve me: I can always count on your help.

What service, what help? You have killed me. I no longer exist. I'm reduced to nothing. Wiped off the face of the earth. You will of course sign the death certificate without any fuss, won't you?

And yet I'm not dead. I didn't keep you from opening the door, did I? Or fall down. Or cling to your lapels, imploring a few minutes' grace. I've done that so many times before. Times enough to be counted like so many sheep. Each a recipe for sleeplessness. Thousands of sheep, all being led to the nearest slaughter-house.

No, I said goodbye. Very correctly. As I was taught. A good obedient little girl. My voice a bit husky. I won't be seeing you again. I know it. And I didn't cry out, weep, stamp my feet or dissolve in mellifluous sobs; no, nothing out of the movies.

I did nothing. A dummy. My "profession" was no help. And my silence denied everything I preach in class: the beauty of the Word, the gift of Poetry—virtue of the word made speech. How I have praised the beauty and eloquence of the vocable! Racine, Corneille. The incomparable clarities. . . . I couldn't repeat a single word of your set piece. You've been holding forth for over an hour. Sixty-seven minutes exactly. Automatically, I noted the time when you began. It was three minutes past three, and a fine clear day. The sun was shining; the ground didn't shake. The face of the earth was not

2

darkened. But I was dead, nailed to the spot with horror. And yet I'm still here, still alive.

Out of all the literature in the world, out of all those books I claim to love, those books I've been solemnly assuring innocent adolescents will help them to forget, to live, to die, there's not a word left me. Not a word, not a thought. Only the same absurd grief felt by one of the girls in Mary McCarthy's *The Group* (a novel I didn't care for) who kept repeating to herself, after her lover had brutally broken with her, "This morning, when we were making love, it was for the last time. And I didn't know." Well, I always wanted to know. Long ago I made this a condition of our parting. You told me I was revolting.

Everything in life is revolting. It is all treason, betrayal. And in time of war, tortured by the enemy, I would have shown the most shameful cowardice, would have betrayed the whole world just to escape suffering.

And here we are in the room. I've turned down the bed. I'm waiting for you. It seems our roles are reversed. I am the executioner now. And you are the terrified unresisting victim.

2

What is this man doing in my room? This stranger who is undressing slowly? For years I've been in love with a phantom that resembled him.

3

A horrible parody. We mimed the movements of love. I reached the bottom of the quagmire. No matter how I tried to fight my way to the surface, I was sucked back into a sickening disgust.

Soil, spoil. *Destroy*, I tell myself. Reach the fag-end of ignominy, of the night. I find my voice again. This whining vulgar voice, it can't be mine. Like some vicious exasperating child's. Or some ugly old woman's, tedious and cloying. I hear my own voice in this rout of our defeated bodies that have no soul within them but only the weight of their wretched flesh. The wheedling voice of the whore on her beat, who knows the worthy well-fed businessman won't stop. To your betrayal, mine is now added. Ridiculous bleating of women no longer loved, women going mad. "You love me? Tell me—you still love me. . . ."

You laughed. As you ought to have. I deserved it. You got dressed again. Swiftly. I said nothing more, made no move. In the doorway, ceremoniously, your last *au revoir*.

The formal words of farewell. I didn't dare watch you going down the stairs, nor wave to you from the balcony: an outworn ritual. But hidden behind the window I still watched. You were running, like a man set free. You jumped into your car without looking back. In a moment you had sped off.

4

Sit on the floor, back to the wall. Not one tear. Now and then a word, a sentence heard in spite of myself, strikes me like another undeserved blow. I hear the bells, ringing out all their changes. Happy bells of Easter, announcing your resurrection. You're a good man again, honest, faithful, upright. At last restored to the bosom of your family. For your greater good. Honour is saved. Virtue is triumphant.

To every holiday its tortures, its sacrifices. Graciously offered at the holy altar. I refuse to be the votive offering, the bleating sheep, the scapegoat.

For ten years I quietly accepted my lot. On the borders of the promised land, in the shadow of the adored Great Man. Without a murmur. A grateful slave. I broke the second commandment, that pitiless law that forbids the making of gods in human shape.

5

Stand up, you idiot. You've been released from your chains, your manacles, your muzzle. Make the most of it now, bellow and scratch. And run. Run far away. Where you'll have no further truck with the sham and tawdry loves of men who have no time, words or tenderness to spare, who belong to their own vaunted clique, the wealthy tribe of the strong from which you were born to be excluded.

6

And Abraham, at the bidding of Sarah, sent Hagar away into the wilderness. With Ishmael. She left without a word of complaint, holding her child by the hand. They say that God watched over them. For me, nothing is left. No child even, made in your image.

I can escape now. Not wait the three days before my sailing. You worked it all out. You still think two months in Venice can cure anything. You're mistaken. I am no character out of Henry James.

I stumble over my half-filled suitcase. Look furtively at the telephone. I've only to dial those magic numbers to re-establish contact.

You'd hate me for that, I know. Really hate me. . . . Stop trying to lie to yourself, you poor fool. He has stopped thinking of you. Or if he does think, it's *what a relief! I'm well rid of her. In the clear now.* While I can barely stir. I feel so old, so defenceless, brittle as glass. I can't recognize my face in the mirror. Marbled cheeks. Livid. No, one's not supposed to go mad for love at my age.

How old was Bérénice? No longer young, I think. I must have foreseen the fate in store for me, since I always liked this tragedy best of all.

In a month, in a year, my lord, how shall we bear
To be divided by so many seas?[1]

If I could only hope, even for a moment, that you too were suffering.

8

From time to time I strike my head against the wall. Shrewd, regular little blows. Like striking a mule. To keep him moving. Time passes. Some hundreds of minutes have gone by without my yielding to the temptation of telephoning you.

You're tired of lying, of this divided existence. I remember something you said. You were sick of this "double life." Cheat! You admit it. *Two loves have I,*[2] as in that stupid song they used to sing in our parents' day.

You've wasted enough time. One must think of serious things. You are forty, with a wife, children and a good position in life. The cards have been dealt.

Ten years from now, when your interlude of chastity is over, you'll be able to go the pace again—faster than ever. With a pretty girl the same age as your daughters.

9

You lied so often to your wife. Not to me. I had no right to such consideration. Even the man condemned to death isn't told the hour of execution.

"I no longer love you."

A plain, bald statement. Pack up and move on, gypsy girl. Make room for those who walk the broad highway. You're in the way. Be off with you. Get lost!

10

Released from the torment of waiting. Thank you, Pierre my gentle lord. Now I am free. Yes, like those blacks in Louisiana when the rich planter, suddenly tired of working his thousands of acres, lets them go. No longer slaves, but free to go wherever they want. To the North, say, to be trodden down in their poverty instead of strung up to the nearest tree. Free! A wretched slave crawling on the ground, begging to be taken back. Oh, then he can be kept on, assured of his pittance, and he'll be able to work twice as hard and without complaining. It will even be all right to whip him if he balks at his tasks. Yet my ancestors took pride in being a "stiff-necked people." You, a real Gentile, can see how well I bend my back. I apostasize on every suitable occasion.

11

Like Job on his dunghill, I make lamentation. God has no hand in my miseries, in my grey, withered, faded innumerable woes. Barrow-loads of dead dry sheets of paper. On this page I tell over my litany of the saints. And you were no saint. You grew weary of the sameness of my cries. All I could do was drone out my love: "I love you, I love you." Like a sick child begging its parents not to go out, not to leave it alone in the dark.

My parents are dead. No more help from them. And indeed they were right to worry about me. "You must learn to defend yourself." With whom, with what? I embraced defeat by following their example.

For me there was only one perfect couple in the world: my own parents. Another Adam and Eve, happy to leave Paradise for Earth and live there free from any prying eye. Safe from the eye of God. Adam and Eve had two children, two enemies. For my parents my birth was also a kind of curse. For them, the divine chastisement was not to bring forth in sorrow but to share their substance with a sickly intruder. At the worst, my mother would have accepted a son, a child made in the image of her beloved. My father could not bear to look at me, this wretched counterfeit of the wife whose beauty he adored.

I was therefore, dear doctor, well prepared to be no more than the shadow of your shadow. But enough.

8

Enough of searching the past, of blaming others. I and I alone am responsible for this mess.

I must brace up. And stop wearing myself out in remorse and regrets. Stand up straight and strong. Resign myself to being only a discarded sketch, a lump of clay in Pygmalion's lumber-room.

After this formal rejection, to set off once again with a firm step. Leaving the city to perish in its flames. Without turning back. Let the wrath of God fall on it. One must go forward, with no backward glance towards the past. Yet when Jehovah wished to save Lot, he bade him take his wife and daughters with him. And despite the company of Lot and the consolation of the children of her womb she did look back, breaking the commandment: a foolish old woman surveying what had been.

Nausea. My body is rebelling against these insults. I cannot stop retching. I am weeping with revulsion. Is this "giving up the ghost"? The ghost then, it's not that dove ascending but these shreds, sticky fragments, loathsome bits, this stench? Giving it up is only a clearance of the body.

12

My love was a paltry thing. A sickly love, a thing of vile chafferings, of giving and getting, as in a cattle market. *Shake on it!* A fragile love not made for storms, a fabric turning from blue to black. I had guaranteed it colour-fast, and at the first washing it smeared.

I am marking time, It is terrible, this going away. If only, all of a sudden, you'd make some move to call me back. As in *Endgame.* The master whistles but the tired slave has gone.

9

I am fooling myself, wantonly. I can *depart in peace.* Flight is better than this shameful stance before a silent telephone.

Suitcases packed and locked. Always this business of unimportant things, of silk and rayon for this dead body that should be draped in sackcloth.

13

Luggage. Passport. I cross the gangway, a traveller like all the others, turning around, confused. Other people's relatives and friends are there, waving their handkerchiefs. I am dreaming. For a moment I thought I saw you among them.

"But Lot's wife looked back, and she became a pillar of salt."

Like that besotted woman, I could wither away in such backward gazing. Through the porthole Montreal looms up mistily. I shall devote the next two months to recording this experience of collapse and flight. I'll force myself to find some meaning in my life through my own words, words to wipe out yours, your cruel sentence of rejection and death. If I find no "extenuating circumstances" I'll put an end to it. "30," as journalists end their copy.

14

I'd like to write absurd novels where I have the leading role and win marvellously airy and graceful triumphs or undergo tragic misfortunes full of ardours and follies. Alas, I'll never write anything but stupid stories without beginning or end, full of strange characters gnawed by obscure sufferings.

15

As a little girl I was neither quaint nor amusing. Like everyone else I'd have liked an audience. But my first entrance misfired. My mother and father went into no ecstasies over my baby charms. The truth was, I upset them. They had no vocation for parenthood. And I had no way of realizing their dreams of the model child, being so little like either of them, so different in every particular, being indeed an odd, a singular number.

My parents were a pair. And they found that enough. I've never known a better matched couple. He and she, and she and he. Like the people in those inanities of Géraldy, one of the few "poets" they admired—perhaps the only one. Even now when I pore over the traces of my pre-history, I find no record of being alone with either of them. Mother and father: always together. I was not jealous of my mother. The idea of being able or even wishing to supplant her never entered my head. Certain Siamese defy any surgical operation: whom God hath joined together. . . . I felt this in my bones. Always they were two—and I, confronting them, was alone.

When I was about five I begged them—without really believing it was possible—to give me a little brother. They laughed heartily. No matter how much I urged them (though only for form's sake)—I knew nothing would change. Hearing their whispers—"There are some mistakes that shouldn't be repeated"—and without quite grasping what was meant, I realized I was the fruit of some "mistake" of theirs. This was a great comfort to me. Ah, they themselves shared the responsibility for my failure! For in their eyes I was definitely not a success. Nor in the eyes of anyone else. Here is the first remark I overheard, swimming up from the depths of my infancy: "She's your own, this child? Surely not." Stoutly, they acknowledged me: "Of course she's ours." The other voice persisted: "She's nothing like her parents." It was true. I had neither their height nor their colouring. And the same voice, or another one, or a thousand others spread over the years, went on sounding the perennial refrain: "That handsome pair. She so fair and he so dark. Marvellous, how they set each other off."

I agreed in finding them handsome. Singly, yes—but above all as a pair who were made to move in concert. They went everywhere hand in hand. And they played together delightfully. Tennis. Games of "catch." On Saturday nights they danced in their favourite nightclubs. And on Sunday mornings, at the Palais de Glace or Molitor, they would waltz on their skates, conscious of being admired. Naturally, spontaneously, their movements were those of a single person.

Of our few walks together I retain only an impression of breathlessness and fatigue. They were constantly obliged to slacken their pace, and I to run as fast as I could. Always trailing at their heels. After a while I would drag my feet. I exasperated them. For them, a "good carriage" was important. Everything I had been denied by nature seemed to be important. I would mutter to myself, "It's easy enough for you, with your long shanks." They were indeed well dowered with legs. I had to stump along on my own little pair of matchsticks. Looking at old photographs, I see I'm not exaggerating. I was feeble, puny. "You must eat." They forced food on me . Every mouthful was a torment. I would swallow obediently, then retire and throw up. "She does it on purpose." It wasn't true, but I gained some respite. After each bout of indigestion I had a few days of peace, of surcease from forced feeding.

Before every outing they took infinite pains to smarten me up for the viewers. "Smarten" was their word. But I had nothing "smart" about me except the miserable fear of failing to please. Far from improving my appearance, their beauty treatments made me still uglier. The results of these efforts, devised by my mother and superintended by my father, were pitiable. I looked like a poodle, all curled and frizzled. And dressed in costly and elaborate clothes which hung on me like old rags. "Nothing suits her." My hair would never stay in place. I looked like a scarecrow, sweating with fear. In fact I spoiled their whole day.

For fashion was their business. All week long they slaved at selling *articles de Paris* which they picked out themselves and discussed interminably at mealtimes. And on Sunday afternoons they took me for walks. Out of the goodness of their hearts. As their bounden duty. I was a shame to them. A living reproach.

Sometimes we met their friends with their own children. Introductions were gone through. I would be squirming. Half dead with shyness. Eyeing the other children enviously. Other people's children had "style," wore their pretty clothes with ease. My own clothes were a travesty. On Sundays it was worse than during the week. For then I had to pretend I was enjoying myself. "Go on, children, play together." The little group would receive me unwillingly, out of politeness. "You don't play the way we do." It was true. I found their games and their jokes stupid. I felt also that I was being judged, weighed, sifted, studied. I would have been rejected out of hand but for that crass magnaminity that makes the handsome accept the homely, for conscience's sake.

One day I found the solution of these Sunday ordeals

by begging to be left at home. "Really, I'd rather play with my own *little girls.*" I had in fact an extraordinary collection of dolls. My parents had spoiled me in this respect. They bought me fine, expensive ones—like my dresses. They never knew how little I cared for them. My favourite doll, the only one really dear to my heart, was a hideous rag creature given me by Madame Voisin the concierge. "Why, that one spoils your whole collection!" But I had my way. By lying. By vociferating, "What will Madame Voisin say?" The argument prevailed. Moreover, they were soon delighted to entrust me to her care.

Madame Voisin was very fond of me. For my own sake. Not for theirs. I was happy in her cubby-hole. Sometimes she asked me to share her "stew-pot." I loved it. My parents couldn't understand my fondness for these "vulgar soups." "Ah, but she can digest them. She has a taste for common stew." They resumed with relief their excursions together. It took *them* only a moment to get ready.

I used to study them, trying to grasp the principles of charm and elegance. But in vain. In the past few years *Marie-Claire, Elle* and other such magazines have been pushing the fashion of matching marital outfits. "For her and for him"—in a wide range of colours. More than thirty years ago, all on their own, my parents chose to harmonize themselves from head to foot. I observed them, happy to be no longer dragged in their wake. Distance in time is always deceitful, but in my child's-eyes they were a couple who sparkled like a fairy-tale, though I couldn't understand why these tales always ended with "and they had many children." I watched them go out, conscious of being the ugly duckling born to this pair of swans who were slim, almost equal in height and who moved with such consummate grace. My mother, with her masses of fair hair, glossy and fluffed out or brought up on her crown in a great coil, with gilded eyelids, a big mouth with glistening teeth and a milky complexion, clear and juicy. And my father, as dark as she was fair, with hair thick and curling, brilliant eyes and beautiful hands, long and slender.

"Go on, you're looking marvellous." I would send them on their way assuring them, "I'll be perfectly all right without you." As soon as the door closed I began my own game. My pretty little girls were seated in their embroidered dresses, all in a row. And facing them the dowdy rag doll who was to give them their lessons through an intermediary.

"Come now, young ladies, behave yourselves. Pay attention! Sit up straight! Silence! Listen!" And I told them all the stories in my head. They had to listen. I made them ask me to repeat what I had said: "Again, again, please. That's a lovely story." Then I made them clap their hands. And so the lesson went on. At that time I hadn't set foot in school, though I dreamed of doing so. No doubt those afternoons with my dolls have made me choose the absurd and delightful profession I practise today. . . . Evening fell. I grew frightened. I turned on the lights. I dragged Julie (that was Madame Voisin's name for my rag doll) into the kitchen. The kitchen, white and enamelled, was more reassuring: it could be surveyed in a single glance. No one was hiding under a bed or in a cupboard. When my parents came back they would protest, "Do you think you're at the Bastille Day fireworks? Electricity costs money, you know." They themselves squandered money on "important things," but didn't approve of "waste."

"But she's such a good girl we mustn't scold her."

By "good" they meant I didn't get in their way. They always wound up with this commendation, though still lauding economy for form's sake.

15

"We aren't rich."

I didn't believe them. They seemed to possess infinite wealth.

Sometimes they allowed themselves to speak of their past. Slyly I led them on. They were unsure how to describe their "early" life. These two, so graceful in motion, were awkward in speech. At first I gathered only scraps and fragments. I detested actual puzzles, but theirs fascinated me. Bit by bit and willy-nilly they revealed their secrets. They had been poor, both of them. His people, oil-and-soap merchants in Toulon, were badly off; they had "bled themselves white" to give him an education.

"Your father went right through high school." His parents had seen him as a civil servant, settled, sure of a pension, looked up to. They had frowned on his "going up to Paris." When he married, they disowned him.

"You see how it was," said my mother. "This good Catholic boy, seduced by a Jewess."

"And a rabbi's daughter to boot," my father added.

"What about your own people?" I asked my mother.

"Why, it was our duty and vocation to be poor. My father wouldn't permit—"

She wasn't allowed to finish. My father cut in, "Her father is a terrible old gentleman whom you'll never see."

I never did see him. No more than I could ever learn, later, in which camp they had liquidated this unyielding parent who refused to see his own daughter or acknowledge his only grand-daughter.

"Your story is so sad."

But they wouldn't hear of it. "It's a very beautiful story." And to convince me they invoked the classics. "When you're older, when you can read, you'll learn the story of Romeo and Juliet. We were the Capulets and Montagues of our day."

16

To marry my father, to be bound to him for ever, to break the bond of religion in a glorious way, my mother wished to be baptized and then married in the church. My father wasn't keen on this, and would not agree. So they didn't stand up before the priest. But they had *me* baptized. The good folk in Toulon made no account of this. Familial relations were confined to sending New Year's greetings. They never came to Paris, and we never went to the Midi.

From time to time the "visitation" took place. My maternal grandmother, braving the veto, would call on us. Once a year, perhaps less often. Mother made preparations for days ahead. On these occasions my father would disappear. It was understood he would vacate the premises when his mother-in-law arrived. Mother, ordinarily little attentive to housework, would engage in a domestic orgy. I trotted behind her, carrying a rag or feather duster. Over and over she kept telling me, "You'll be good. You won't bother her. You won't say anything."

"Anything about what?"

"About what you eat, for instance."

"But I eat whatever you give me."

Mother sighed. "Say as little as you can."

The bare idea of this irascible old woman frightened me to death.

On her first visit I must have been five. I was amazed. I had been expecting a kind of virago. A little old lady, frail and wrinkled, came in. At once the atmosphere of the house was transformed. She murmured vague greetings. Mother, for her part, spoke louder than usual. For the first time I found her ill at ease, vulnerable, on the defensive.

"Come in. Don't be alarmed. You won't run into any crucifixes or holy-water basins."

My grandmother said nothing. She looked at me. No

17

one had ever looked at me like this. I did not feel I was being judged, measured, compared, but rather pierced to the heart. And I, the shy one, made the first advances. I dared to call her Granny. The day before I had asked my mother, "What shall I call your mother? 'Granny'?" She made no reply.

"How do you do, Granny. I am glad to see you. You know, I often tell myself beautiful sad stories."

I had never said so much to anyone. My mother, dithering, was about to interpose. My grandmother made a gesture. She kept looking at me. Her eyes, small and sparkling, must have once been black, but now had the strange colour of slate. Slowly, they filled with tears. And these tears, very big, began to pour down her cheeks while she continued to fix me with her soft gaze. I left them together, mother and daughter. I didn't hear them utter a word. From time to time my grandmother dabbed at her eyes with a handkerchief whose dazzling whiteness contrasted with her black mourning dress. For she was dressed in black every time she came. And the same ceremony was repeated, year after year. A few words at the door; then the tears falling softly and regularly; at last, some vague sentences as she left. She made no demands on us, did not touch us except with that gaze of hers, that tactile gaze which disturbed me as much as it had the first time. But I never repeated my daring initial act of speech, and contented myself with looking straight into her eyes.

Even today I could draw, from memory, those eyes at once so sad and so alive, underlined with blueish grey and ringed with salmon pink. After her visits, a constraint weighed on the house. We did not exchange a word for some time after she left. Except the very last time, before we left France. I was ten. I could not resist sharing my discovery.

"It's funny. People still say I don't look like you. Now I know why. It's because I look like your mother." Mother tried to deny it: "I don't see . . ." But I insisted: "I know. I'm sure of it." She questioned me eagerly: "Who told you? Was it she herself?" I was astonished. "Why, of course not. I only thought of it just now, when I saw her going out." Then my mother confided to me, "Strange, she told me the same thing the first time she saw you. You were four or five."

"What did she tell you?"

"Only this: 'Your daughter looks like me.' "

I didn't press her further. To spare her feelings, and as a kind of recompense for this admission which I felt had wounded her. I hid my own dismay. I had a presentiment of a long chain of sorrows bequeathed me out of a distant past. My mother had tried to break this chain. She failed. I had re-forged the link.

16

Turning over these memories doesn't hurt me. On the contrary, they give me reason to hope. Having seen my grandmother weep so much, with such fluency, so much quiet abandon, I restrain my own tears over this banal love affair of ours.

17

It isn't true to say that you alone could make me happy. Did I tell you that? I lied. For my purest and truest joys, I owe you nothing.

I see that I have forgotten and lost forever the most precious and apocalyptic moments of my life. I wished passionately to go to school. My parents were hesitant, fearing my shyness, my inability to get along with others. On the first day of school they went with me, multiplying their counsels. I scarcely listened. I left them "courageously," as they told me later.

To tell the truth, I needed no courage to go to school. I only wished to be there. The day passed like lightning. I did as I was told, rising and sitting down obediently, one of the crowd. One set of rules governed us all. I didn't know what it was all about, any more than the others. But I was discovering a new equality, and I listened eagerly, without the least fatigue. Here, the world was being offered me, and I was ready for any drudgery that would bring me its treasures. I formed my pothooks with delight, sang in chorus with the rest: *do re mi.*

One day, I could read. I can't recall the exact moment of this sudden leap, this entrance into the life of the mind. Just as I have forgotten the first book I read right through, following the unexpected marvels of the story itself, disregarding the stupid instructions of the primer with its frightful little illustrations. How ungrateful one's memory is! From that day on, my life was changed. I was no longer alone. With me, now and for all time, was the comforting presence of the world of print. I devoured this world. Until then I had felt isolated, painfully composing those fragile scenarios for my dolls. Now, adventures fetched from the four corners of the earth and from the most remote ages, were mine. A transformation of my entire being.

In the same way, I can no longer recall the exact

moment when you decided to cease loving me. For me, it was a swift passage from a kind of happiness to a foreordained damnation; for you, a deliberate decision which you have just announced—officially, so to speak. No, I can't recall the bitter taste of those carefully chosen words of yours. There was nothing I could say. There is never anything to say when one is dismissed. I'm writing this book only to soften the impact of the truth. Every night I pick my way through tortuous dreams where you are trying to come back to me.

19

I have no gift for joy. It slips through my fingers. As a distraction from my suffering I would like to recall those wonderful hours of my childhood when I found my first genuine happiness. Given me once and for all, and never to be taken away. If I were blind, I would learn Braille; in prison, I would run to the library. Alas, in ordinary misfortunes this escape is cut off. Lucky Montaigne! When I am suffering, no "fifteen minutes' reading" brings me relief. On the contrary, I *cannot* read. Wearily I go from bookshelf to bookshelf, fingering one volume after another. None of them has any meaning. So I go back to my task of writing here. One word after another. I'm ready to do anything at all, as always, to escape my servitude. Quietly spelling out the *do re mi* of my suffering. And praying that my deliverance is not too far off.

20

I liked school. I found my place in the class. Not first, but in the first rank. Sometimes I was teacher's pet, as the other girls ungrudgingly allowed. Best of all, I was accepted.

I had made a friend, a funny little girl with a head as round as a billiard ball and covered with soft, sparse hair, and with big astonished eyes, also round. Her name was Nadine. We came together by chance. My parents had kept up their regime of over-feeding me: for every daily recess they prepared a veritable feast. I was trapped between my loathing for buttered rolls and the fear of throwing them away. "Never throw away a crust of bread." Strangely enough, my mother and father, each brought up so differently, shared this domestic taboo. They observed it rigorously. Even our breadcrumbs were gathered in a kind of silver scoop and distributed to the sparrows. Not thrown away, but doled out like an alms. Seeing me hesitate to cut into my roll, Nadine said to me enviously, "Lucky you. You've always lots of goodies."

"What about you?"

"Mamma says I'm too fat. All day long I'm simply starving."

I was flabbergasted. The more so since poor little Nadine, except for her spherical head, seemed ill-nourished. She wolfed my rolls. It became a rite. Every day, at eleven and three o'clock, Nadine fell on my food—rolls, bananas, cake—and continued to look thin and famished.

"I've a little sister. Mamma loves her better than me. She doesn't like me at all. My father is dead. My sister, she's my stepfather's little girl."

I asked Nadine to our house. She devoured everything in sight. My parents crammed her with sweets. We would play complicated games invented by me. Already, at the age of seven—even though I had a free choice of subjects and themes—I deliberately sought the secondary role of the spurned or sacrificed woman: good, but weak. I was the poor princess on whose head calamities descended. And Nadine impersonated the wicked queen who persecuted her. But I wanted to play fair: I enjoyed my chosen role so much that I offered to exchange it for hers. She refused. It was clear that she was enjoying herself as much as I.

I met her mother only once. "Mamma says I can have you in on Thursday."

My visit was a disaster. Her mother was an immense gaunt woman who paralysed me with fright. Nadine's sister was a little pest who stood in front of us making faces. I upset the glass of lemonade given me. The tumbler broke.

"How clumsy you are," her mother exclaimed.

At home, no one had ever spoken to me like this.

Blushing scarlet, Nadine tried to make excuses for me: "She didn't do it on purpose." To my great relief I wasn't invited again. Nadine continued coming to our house.

"Doesn't it bother your parents my being always at your place?"

I assured her they preferred to know we were there together.

At our place too, we followed a ritual. Every Thursday we staged our show against a background which seldom changed. After that we would try out new recipes for custards and creams, often failures, but which Nadine swallowed with ecstasy. And there was always school, and reading. Jules Verne, Dumas, books by Zénaïde Fleuriot; the *Semaine de Suzette* series; the Collection Verte, the Bibliothèque Rose. I soaked myself in them happily, impervious to anything else. On Sundays I went to my room to read, giving the excuse of extra homework. My life was regulated. Happy. Calm. The dolls had given way to books. I arranged my books around me with the passion of a miser. There, under my hand, were the beloved treasures with their exquisite passages of highflown melancholy which I would read and re-read, shedding many tears. Nothing else touched me. Though never physically hungry, I felt the pangs of starvation when I read the descriptions of banquets; terrified of the smallest insect or the most harmless animal, I dreamed of lion hunts and polar explorations. I lived only in this paper world, and did my schoolwork only so I could savour the blessings of fiction in peace.

"You are mad, you'll wear your eyes out."

My parents no longer opposed me. On "special occasions" they would give me the books I had marked on carefully prepared lists. During these years nothing else affected me. I neither saw nor heard anything, lost among my dreams, lost in torrents of the printed word. I was living by proxy.

No matter how the real world might appear to threaten or encroach, I refused to pay it any heed. I no longer even saw my parents, who had lately been trying to re-establish contact with me.

"You're ten now, you're a big girl."

I refused to listen. Without thinking to ask why, I noticed they were not going out so often nor so light-heartedly. They listened to the radio, brought home stacks of newspapers. I was forbidden to read the news, and I obeyed. In any case, the news of the world meant nothing to me. For hours on end my mother would listen to Hitler ranting on the short wave. She would translate bits for my father, her voice trembling. "He is a madman. We must leave. At once. There's barely time."

The sound of their voices would filter through the door of their room. They were plunged now in interminable discussions. A few words reached me. "Fatherland... deserter . . . impossible." That was my father. Mother spoke in a lower tone and at greater length. One day I went in when they were finishing an argument. Mother was in tears. This was in 1938. Just after Munich.

"I've betrayed *my* people too—as you put it, if we must use big words. I chose you for my husband. And now you want to leave me. For a filthy war. You lied to me. You swore you weren't just another vindictive little Frenchman like the rest of them." She stopped when she saw me. But then she returned to the charge with fresh tears. Desperately, she tried to enlist me on her side.

"Wouldn't you like to leave here for America? A beautiful brand-new country. A paradise for children." I said nothing. The very idea of going away upset me. All I asked was to keep on living in my own little niche. I shrank from all change or movement. I needed nothing more from life. It was enough for me, just as it was.

21

You see, I've never been grasping. I've always observed the speed limit. That's my own little portion of wisdom, my only wealth. You didn't see that my whole happiness was made out of the bits and pieces of your own life. On the pretext of "justice" you made me give them up. And so you took from me the little I had.

22

I refused to arbitrate between my parents. Besides, I had no illusions of the influence of any words of mine. My mother must have been panic-stricken to use such arguments. I said nothing. I hid my despair. To leave everything I loved! School, my books, Nadine, my own room. I counted them up. And then I was astonished to find the list so short. Other little girls possessed infinitely greater riches. Bevies of cousins, aunts, relatives of all ages, pet animals, summers in the country. Conscious of the dearth of my own possessions, I clung to them all the more fiercely.

So I said nothing. Then I tried to put myself in their place. My father's reasons struck me as irrefutable. They were in harmony with the ideas in books. Duty, honour, Corneille, defense of the homeland; the man at the front, the woman at home, quietly weeping. Mother was no doubt unreasonable to reject the common lot, the path of duty. But she had some justice on her side too. And the pledges of love. Long ago Mother had made her choice. My grandmother's tears confirmed it. I was unable to decide.

My father ended by yielding. Gaily, my mother sold off the furniture. It was then I realized that my parents, with their few shop-made sticks of furniture, were not rich. It was all they had. And my books, of course. I made no complaint.

"You've read them all a dozen times. Over there, you'll have a real young lady's library."

All the same, I loved my books.

At mealtimes my parents now spoke nothing but English, as a preparation for New York. I said goodbye to Nadine, to the school, to the other pupils. They envied me. "Such a lovely trip! What an adventure!" I played my part. I kept smiling. If I had listened to myself I would have ground my teeth in despair. I always knew I could do nothing to change things.

23

I envy the children of today. My own students this autumn, with their fervent protests: hoping to change the order of things, and all the established orders. In my day that was unthinkable. In that world of yesterday there was no rebellion, no way out. The only conceivable refusals were made in silence. I was a silent child. You, Pierre, are in luck. I was trained to obey. To "take it." Not to make scenes. Yet I had within me all the resources of a tragic actress. I could have played with great *brio* the scene of the lovers' parting in Act V.

24

We sailed on the 20th of December, 1938. With a couple of trunks and several suitcases. Everything happened so swiftly I could still hardly believe it. When the ship left the dock I had to accept the fact. I took refuge in nausea. Throughout the voyage I was seasick. My parents took turns at my bedside, basin in hand, glad to keep busy even at this revolting task.

At the moment of sailing they had been unable to hide their feelings. Ordinarily so reserved, they had fallen into each other's arms. After this embrace my father wept. I had never thought that in real life a man was capable of tears. It disturbed me deeply.

"Now we are immigrants," he said.

"We'll get used to it," said Mother bravely. She alone of all the passengers did not fix her eyes on the coastline but kept looking resolutely at the open sea. Looking ahead.

"We're going to be very happy in America."

The landing was miserable. Cold, with a frightful wind. No one could understand the broken English my father and I kept jabbering. Mother took over. She made all the arrangements and settled us in a furnished apartment on the fifth floor of a brick building somewhere west of Broadway. It looked on an air-shaft. High up as we were, not a ray of light reached us all day long.

"It's only for the time being."

There were two rooms, a kind of kitchen and a tiny bathroom. I slept in the "living-room." My surroundings had never affected me, but here they seemed ominous. I spent all day in the apartment. My parents ran around looking for the "gold mine" that would make them rich.

"You'll soon see how happy we're going to be."

I no longer believed them.

"As soon as we get jobs we'll put you in a nice school."

I stayed by the high window, reading my new books over and over. I already knew them by heart. I didn't dare look down, from my fear of heights. The sky was invisible. They had told me not to go too far from home. There was no need: the city terrified me. I went only to the corner grocery store to buy what we needed for the evening meal. I prepared this as well as I could. They would come in late, dead tired and dishevelled. "Nothing yet." And then the old refrain, "We mustn't touch our capital." Their appearance spoke for itself. They had altered. Less brilliant, less alive, their clothes wrinkled. Their very skin showed the wear and tear. These signs of fatigue brought them closer to me.

I tried to bring some order into the two rooms. But the dust returned as soon as I wiped it away. It had a vile smell, of coal and urine mixed. Javel-water hid nothing, added only another revolting odour. On the day I bought

some flowers at half-price—three half withered car-
nations—they made a scene.

"Do you think we're millionaires?"

Since our arrival in America I found their manners had
coarsened. Nettled to see my good intentions bring down
such an undeserved rebuke, I passed to the attack: "Your
American paradise doesn't seem to be improving you."

My father nearly struck me. Mother interposed.

"She's right."

He controlled himself. They were finding it harder
than ever to preserve an air of calm. After that, I stopped
trying to improve things.

In Paris they had warned me against so many things.
Kidnapping, rapes, children sliced up like salmon
steaks—these things fascinated them. They translated
them into terms suitable to my age. Even playing hop-
scotch on the sidewalk was risky, even dangerous. I had
strict orders to keep the front door on the chain. Never to
let a stranger in. In New York they had given me no such
orders. In any case, the door had neither chain nor spy-
hole. When the bell rang one afternoon I opened the
door. I regretted it immediately. An oldish man with a
grey beard, very dirty, pushed in. In my halting English I
tried to explain his mistake. To my dismay I saw that he
realized I was alone. He closed the door behind him
carefully. He advanced. I retreated. He seized me. His
hands were everywhere. I pushed him away in horror. He
threw me down on the couch that served me for a bed. I
felt his weight, smelled his breath of garlic and alcohol,
saw his purplish scabbed lips coming close to my own. I
was unable to utter a sound. With my teeth and thighs
locked together, I kept pummelling him with all my
strength. He was laughing.

"We're going to play mummy and daddy . . ."

This phrase, spoken with a giggle and completing my

horror, gave me the strength to cry out. But for that expression I would have let myself be forced. I gave a scream. He tried to silence me. I bit his hand. He laughed still louder.

"Don't be scared. Come on, let's play." And he kept repeating "mummy and daddy" in a high piping voice. I was covered with sweat, exhausted. Then he began slapping my face, the blows resounding in my head. He found this funnier than ever. All at once he stopped. Had he heard someone coming? I've no idea. He signed to me to be quiet. I obeyed, and he left.

Once the door had closed behind him my teeth began to chatter. I was frozen with disgust. Bending over the toilet, I made myself vomit. I thought I was dying. I wanted to die—so as not to have to face anyone, and I leaned out over the window-ledge. But it was too high, too black, too dirty. . . . Having no other refuge I opened up the couch, the scene of that horrible encounter. I got into bed and pulled the covers over my head. When my parents returned I pretended to be asleep.

"She's burning hot," Mother declared.

For several days I shammed sickness, in order not to move, speak, go out. Perhaps I was really ill. My parents became worried. I passed hours without making a single movement. Waiting for the passage of time. I scarcely answered their questions. In fact I held this experience against them. For not having spared me this hideous thing. For having left me alone, at the mercy of no matter what, between these sinister grey walls.

And now, whenever their bedroom door closed behind them, I began to tremble. With disgust. With curiosity. On any pretext at all I would call to them. One of them would get up to attend to me or tuck me in. I studied them. They had not changed. Just a little drowsy looking. It was unthinkable that behind that closed door they too

30

had been playing the same vile game. I tried to pull myself together, to drive from my memory that brutal scene and its details which were constantly multiplying. Recalling all the workings and writhings of that assault, I was overcome by nausea.

For long afterwards certain male looks, gestures and intonations made my heart skip a beat. Behind them all I saw that other gaze, foggy and flickering, those brutal hands, that disgusting voice. I felt I had been abandoned, soiled, possessed against my will.

26

I repressed this memory for years. The men I met reminded me of it. The slightest gesture would re-create my terror. With you, I was free of all that. I thought I was safe. And you hurt me more than any of them.

27

My parents were once more radiant. They had happened to meet a former acquaintance who proposed they manage a fancy-goods shop in Montreal. Eagerly, they packed their trunks again.

"Canada, that will be much better. They speak French there. And the air in New York doesn't suit the child."

We had spent three months in this city, which seemed to me like centuries. I was glad to go.

Here's how I arrived in this country of yours: in the middle of a beautiful March snowstorm! Everything white, clean, invigorating. The air was crisp. The sunlight glittered on the snow. I could breathe more easily. After New York, this was almost like the countryside. There were trees. And children playing everywhere on the sidewalks, in perfect freedom. Even the babies were tumbling in the snowbanks. It was reassuring to see them left to themselves like this. The city must be quite safe.

My parents' immediate concern was for me.

"First, we'll find a place for her. Then we'll be free to work."

They inquired about schooling. At that time the secondary schools were all run by the religious orders.

"Well, why not? She's been baptized. And she wants to make her first communion. There's no problem."

I had indeed attended the classes in religion at the *lycée*. Just to be like the others, like Nadine.

Neither my mother nor father liked the idea of "reporting to the nuns," as they put it. They decided to go together, properly "made up" for the occasion.

"Won't we make a splendid pair of good little bourgeois believers!"

They were laughing. I too laughed merrily. My father put on his darkest suit. Mother made herself a kind of turban which hid her hair. They were barely recognizable.

29

I decided to follow their lead. I too would change. I was brimful of good resolutions to transform myself in deference to this new world. To present the proper image. I always had a fund of natural foolery, a kind of imitation goodwill, ready for any role in fancy dress. To please you too, dear doctor, I often wore ridiculous clothes. When I saw you were tired of one disguise I assumed another, not realizing it was myself you were rejecting. The costume matters little when the character lacks interest.

30

What does all this "history" matter, this past only less hideous than the present? Even as I unwind the skein, the thread escapes me. As if I were telling the story of someone else. This awkward, insignificant little girl is no longer myself, though she resembles me in a few uncouth traits. At present I am at once stronger and infinitely more vulnerable. In those days I was not the active instrument of my fate. Today, I see that I myself have chosen this trap I'm in and have embraced a thousand humiliations to remain there. I am still ready for unconditional surrender, if it would only restore me to favour.

31

The road of the past is less painful to follow than the one that lies ahead. So I resume the former, only regretting I have no Bible to hand. For I would like to know why God saw fit to save Lot and his daughters if only they would not look back on their city in flames. I understand Lot's wife all too well.

I too, at this summer's end, may perhaps be turned —through shedding so many tears over the past—to another pillar of salt.

Well, let God repeat himself. Let him strike down another woman who in her crazed and desperate flight keeps regretting a dead past and a forbidden love. How can I flee into the future when my affections and desires draw me always backward? I laugh at the future. I leave it to others. If I understand things correctly, Lot left his wife in the lurch, poor woman. Because of her curiosity? I doubt it. Perhaps because of her compassion. He himself did not look back. And there he was, free, disencumbered. Able to enjoy the life of a merry widower.

I cannot fix my gaze on my own future. Nothing there is bearable. I envy the fate of those whom death strikes swiftly. Tirelessly I recall the past and my rejected love. What is this merciless God doing? Why, he's punishing me by letting me live.

32

"The sisters have decided to take you after the Easter holidays. They promised to see you won't miss your year."

"They're quite nice," Mother added. "A bit supercilious. Prim. But nice. Now, don't forget to say, 'Yes, Mother, no, Mother': that's the way to address them." She had soon learned. I promised to imitate her. " 'Yes, Mother, no, Mother,' " I simpered. Mother approved. Together, we bought the black school uniform. I donned it with pleasure. My mother gave a cry of horror. Delighted with this lugubrious garment, I told her, "It's just the thing, it won't show the dirt."

I entered the school. The sisters also struck me as "nice," imprisoned as they were in their embroidered chokers and long funereal robes. One had to call them all

"Mother." Fortunately for me. Because for a long time I found they all looked exactly alike.

"You're crazy," my schoolmates exclaimed. "Imagine confusing Mère du Saint-Sacrement with Mère des Saints-Anges! You can't be serious."

For some racists all black people, and all yellow people, look the same: they're all dinges or chinks. Whatever their age or features. I must have been a racist in my own little way.

My schoolmates were easy to get along with. At first they laughed at my accent. "Come on now, you're putting it on."

But they soon helped me to adjust. Thanks to their "tips" I made none of the blunders which neither Mother nor I could have foreseen. One day when I was talking about the books I liked, they motioned me to silence. One of the "Mothers" was looming.

"We're not allowed to read those books?"

"Not exactly, but it comes to the same thing."

I had in fact given up reading the "recommended" works and "allowed readings" in the school library. For all my appetite for the printed word, which made me accept almost anything, I could work up no interest in such drivel.

"Do like us. Read in secret."

One had to lie about everything, so I lied.

We were obliged to "approach the sacraments" frequently. Any freedom of choice was barely tolerated, independent thinking closely watched. I soon adopted the conventional stance.

One tie alone bound me to my little fellow pupils. We were united in a communion of obligatory falsehood. Lies, half-lies, wilful omissions. In France I would not have dared twist the truth knowingly. Not so much from

35

any sense of morality as from the absolute assurance of being immediately found out. Our teachers there —clever, resourceful women—were more concerned with our opinions. They encouraged us to have "original ideas."

"Think for yourselves!" one of them would exclaim whenever we handed in compositions that were too "banal."

Here it was just the other way round. "Why can't you do like everyone else? Repeat the lesson word for word."

I took infinite pains to vary the formulas.

"Why try to *improve* on everything? The text is perfect, just as it is."

One had, therefore, to repeat "perfectly" the résumés of the lesson. Even to the periods and commas. The closer our recitations were to the original, the more "perfect" they were. We fooled perfection to the top of our bent. The less effort I made, the better I succeeded. The temptation to do so was great, and I succumbed. This curious perfection of response allowed one to achieve a kind of detachment, by touching things only superficially. To enumerate them, but never to turn them over or examine them. Above all, to ask no questions. At first I did ask them.

"You're crazy. You're simply provoking them. They don't understand a word of what they're dinning into us. They go by the book, that's all."

The master's book, the pupil's manual. Questions and answers. Like the catechism.

Such ignorance on their part seemed incredible. But indeed the slightest, most harmless question put them out of countenance. Ordinarily they were pale and colourless. This had struck me from the beginning. Those bloodless cheeks, lifeless eyes, lipless mouths. That gaze so constrained, reserved, dead. When one asked them a question the calm was broken. They reddened, grew uneasy. Then they took the offensive.

"You mean I did not explain the first time?"

I gave up.

At this time Danielle Guillaume was already my friend. I found her brilliant both for her beauty and her intelligence. I admired her rebellion against "those fools of sisters," as she already called them at the age of twelve. I myself had grasped the fact that such "fools" were simply creatures crazed and made cruel by fear. I was sure I was not mistaken. Long ago I had felt, in my inmost being, what bound me to my grandmother. The same phenomenon was being repeated: between the sisters and myself, this strange kinship. They feared not only our questions but everything that threatened to shatter their fragile self-confidence. They were only at ease inside the convent walls and the cage of their uniform. Behind the blinkers of their headbands they felt safe, half blinded and assuredly deaf. And with their bodies lost, forgotten, hidden in the black straitjacket which warded them from others and from themselves. So encased, they were no longer liable to the least contact. With every word ritually strained and filtered, every movement smothered.

One day I nearly lost my balance. Instinctively I sought to cling to one of them. Just as instinctively she recoiled a step. I fell. She recovered herself and took me to the infirmary where she saw to me. But in that instant I had seen the fear in her face, the horror of proximity, of all fleshly contact. I remembered New York. I saw now why the sisters were where they were. Out of circulation. Out of the storm. And even we, little girls as we were and far removed from any overt rebellion or premeditated mutiny, we frightened them. We were still a part of life. We planned to "pass our life in the world," as they scornfully put it. They were frightened of the coquettes, of the girls who "wanted to know." Even the studious girls alarmed them. I tried to reassure them about myself. "The little French girl," as they had called me to begin with, only wished to escape notice.

They looked askance at my friendship with that "headstrong" Danielle. They didn't dare persecute her openly, for in her they respected the reputation of her father, one of the leading physicians in Montreal. Danielle taxed me with my excessive docility. I would have let myself be torn in pieces before confessing my real weakness to her. Yes, I was as cowardly as the "mothers" themselves. They had chosen the grilles of the cloister for a sanctuary. I had taken refuge in the "wicked" books which might have had me expelled. But for a long time this paper screen had served me as an alibi, a "front." I lived my fictive lives in many a novel. I avoided living my own. As for that little portion of joys and sorrows given to everyone, I willingly renounced it. And here I am at the age of forty, without a child, without the man I used to love.

33

The very word "lover" filled them with horror. Even in those tragedies of the seventeenth century they kept trying to conjure it away. And they obliged us, each time it turned up, to verify its "real" meaning in the notes at the back of the book in order to assure ourselves of its perfect innocence in the context. A woman who had a lover was irremediably "lost."

What sermons we had on chastity, modesty, purity! More than enough to implant "wicked" thoughts in the most innocent mind. I sensed their fear of the flesh. It has so long been my own that I can recognize it in desiccated virgins as well as in those mothers who, swamped with children, still have a horror of the Thing. These "mothers," poor mothers without children, had no love for us. I knew it by instinct.

I had a long adolescence, ruled by fear and fascination. Fear was uppermost. It would be easy to blame heredity, environment, circumstances. My fear of violence, of death. Of love. Fear of suffering. Fear of being afraid. I had to read the *Dialogue des Carmelites*[3] to understand I was not a wretched exception in the world of women. But even Blanche de la Force had found in her weakness a guarantee of her safety.

I thought this love of ours would be my guarantee, my protection. Yet from the very first day I was afraid of losing you. And also, like Blanche casting her horoscopes in childhood, I was afraid of entering the genuine life of passion. Today, I am enduring its torments.

34

The happiness of my parents was contagious. Delighted with their new employment, they acquired friends. And with their increased and glowing *joie de vivre* they found themselves more in love than ever. They announced jubilantly, "We're having our second honeymoon in Canada." Adding kindly, "with our little girl."

They had taken an apartment which I found quite perfect. I had my own room. Everything was bright and modern. I forgot the phantoms of the past. They decided, towards the end of summer, to take me with them on their holidays. I looked forward to this, and was not disappointed. I watched them swim, dive and sunbathe from morning to night by the lake where they had rented a tiny cottage for two weeks. I loved the silence at night, the brilliant daylong sunlight, the calm water which I began to brave all by myself. Just then the war broke out. Mother simply exclaimed, at once and emphatically, "Ah, we did the right thing."

35

The war didn't seem to upset anyone, at least in the circles where I moved. The "phoney" war settled in. The French soldiers were firmly ensconced behind the Maginot Line.

"You see," said my mother, "one man more or less playing Zouave would have made no difference."

My father said nothing. I wondered what he was thinking. Was he tortured by remorse? Better not to ask. He had made friends with other French citizens of his own age in Montreal. They talked of nothing but business, *les affaires*.

Then it was 1940. The invasion, the bombings, the fall of Paris, Vichy. To my father, who still remained silent, Mother kept asserting the wisdom of their choice. "Can't you see us, the child and me, on the roads being machine-gunned on one of those terrible marches? And you, a prisoner of war in Germany. Perhaps for years."

Those millions of prisoners of war seemed to fascinate her. There was no more talk of *résistance*. In Canada the war effort was stepped up. But we, behind the walls of the convent school, were shut off from the distant murmur of life and death alike.

For us it was the beginning of adolescence: we were in our teens. The only thing that touched me was the news of my grandmother's death. Mother's eyes were red for several days. That was all.

Nonsense. A mass of girlish nonsense filled my fifteenth year. Studies took a back seat. Gossiping with the girls was all that mattered. Interminably, we talked about boys. And if by any chance we met one, we would giggle. Not to have menstruated was a deviation. Not to be frontally "developed" was a catastrophe. And at this girlish harvest, so long awaited, I reaped none of the desired attributes. My "top" was still non-existent, my "bottom" was assuming alarming proportions. A most unlucky distribution. What was to be done? At this point I grew aware of the lacunae in literature. Juliet had only to appear to make Romeo fall for her, and she was just my age. O melancholy, deceptive age! My mother was aware of my "backwardness." For want of similar retarded heroines in classical fiction or the drama, her maternal wisdom invoked certain family precedents. Some cousin or other had once waited until she was sixteen, possibly seventeen, for her periods. The very fact that my mother, otherwise so forgetful of dates and details, had remembered this case was an indication of its rarity and the importance she had placed on it.

According to my mother, one had to be fit, never "out of sorts" like the common herd of women whom she wholeheartedly despised for their "female ailments"—ailments that they used as a buckler against the "realities" of woman's lot. For me, the knowledge that I was breaking with a long family tradition of sexual precocity was doubly miserable. My beloved books were no help now. In the domain of print I "opted" for the popular magazines. My problem was aired there, along with a hundred others like it.

At last I became officially a young lady. I cheerfully endured the monthly nuisance, delighted to have passed this stage on the road to womanhood. And I recovered a portion of happiness when one of my comrades declared that I had the prettiest pair of legs in the class. To have the prettiest anything, no matter what, seemed an unhoped for piece of luck. My heroines became Mistinguett and Marlene. If they could build a career on the beauty of their calves, I felt reassured about my own prospects. A nice "penniless young man" would starve himself in order to offer me the luxury of "sheathing them in silk." We were idiots.

Our schoolwork suffered. All kinds of competitions were organized where we compared, with measurements carefully noted, our respective "development." Only two or three "swots" scorned these beauty contests. "They know they don't stand a chance," snickered the others who, besides, were smart enough to arrange that the same girl never came last twice in succession. Was this kindness of heart? Or unwillingness to lose too many entrants? The consolation prizes were carefully distributed. Obviously they were the only ones I could hope for. Once, and once only, I came first. I vaguely suspected a cabal among the judges, headed by my friend Danielle who seemed determined to see me "get back my self-confidence."

Thereafter, under her direction, I spent my pocket money on rosewater and witch-hazel, face-creams and wonder-working soaps. No longer on books. In the privacy of my room I smeared myself with ointments, engaged in all kinds of exhausting scientific exercises designed to distribute my muscles and flesh in a more aesthetic proportion, that is, in the right places. The results were neither rapid nor convincing.

My parents found me tiresome. Out of modesty, instead of invoking the cause of beauty I alleged the excuse of health. Armed with a few dietetic theories picked up at random, I regularized our casual eating habits. I found an unexpected ally in my mother. Stewed fruit, grated carrots, lemon juice, grapefruit now appeared at our meals. My father was furious. Mother played the good parent, studious of the "always precarious metabolism of growing girls." At this difficult period of my own "awkward age," she herself had reached the painful point of that fortieth year which I have reached today. My ideas gave her a fine excuse to go unobtrusively on the same diet herself.

"We mustn't set the girl a bad example."

With some annoyance my father submitted to our fads.

That was the year I discovered "adult" movies. Until then there had been only Charlie Chaplin, the revolting Snow White, and Shirley Temple with her ringlets. One had to arrange an exchange of identity cards with the "big girls" of sixteen in order to enter this cinematic paradise whose charms were increased tenfold by the thrill of illegality. Thus, two years before the age allowed by law, one gained an introduction to "real life." And there, as far as I was concerned, the only life worth living was played out. On the screen grown men and women fleshed out those stories of consuming and sublime passions "unto death" which on paper, according to my parents, were simply "romances."

At first my parents demurred.

"But Danielle goes."

For me, the argument was conclusive. Mother backed me up. "For once, she won't be keeping to herself." Father ended by yielding, only adding, "But it's not right—in war time." Mother interposed sharply: "We came to Canada just so *she* would escape all that."

While they were exchanging these pious falsehoods I dared not look at them. Lately they had been trying to persuade themselves they had "chosen exile" for my sake.

43

Without altogether blaming them, I found this excuse specious. After all, had their leaving France been so wrong? Almost everyone I knew was against the war. Refusal to "go" was, in French Canada, a claim to distinction. I had no wish to decide between them, or to judge them. But this insincerity of theirs seemed to me like an admission of moral uncertainty. So by common consent we avoided any frank discussion of the subject.

A new bond was forming among the three of us. They had always had a horror of the sickly infant who had shackled them, of the awkward child who had so disappointed them. But the *jeune fille* I was becoming, this moved them. I was their whole past, and they foresaw a glowing future for me. They congratulated themselves on my "transformation."

"She's becoming quite fetching."

"She's settling down."

"She has stopped wool-gathering."

For my benefit they piled on the charm, as if I were an outsider. All they asked was that I meet them half-way, treat them less as parents than as comrades.

Strange, these divisions of age. I was preparing to cross one of mine, and they were terrified of leaving one of theirs. The youth that stretched before me was what they were leaving behind. They hoped to prolong their own, through me.

"Have a boy friend in on Sunday, if you like. We could go for a run in the car, the four of us."

I invented obstacles. The very idea of coquetting before my parents horrified me. If *they* had forgotten the distance between us, I had not. I had not crossed the magic threshhold of sex. They slept together, while I lay in my own room, alone, dreaming more or less innocently.

They were astonished by my modesty. Hastily, I

would set down the breakfast tray in their bedroom in obedience to the ritual Sabbath service on which they insisted. I performed this duty every Sunday, bringing them the well-worn "surprise" of tea and toast.

"Don't go. Bring your own cup."

I did nothing of the kind. I closed the door carefully behind me, shutting off the odour of their intimacy.

The smell of "grown-ups" had always filled me with distaste, even long ago in Paris. For me, everything physical turned to something bitter and strange, after a certain age. Horror of the hair on hands, of the jelly of breasts. My own cigarettes, smoked in secret, had a delicious savour. With adults it became the reek of old butts. Food and drink turned their breath to a kind of oily blast. Their clothing had the clinging taint of fried food and cigars.

When Mother asked me to make "their" bed, I secretly wished to be spared this indecency.

"Pull up the sheets."

I could touch them only with my fingertips. Sometimes my parents would appear without their dressing-gowns. Couldn't they cover up, hide themselves? From my reading I know that the children in books have exquisite olfactory memories of maternal furs and scents. Not I. As a child I found all adult scents at once frightening and disgusting. I discerned in them a kind of horrible decay, like the "well hung" game I always refused to taste. Not until I read Zola, with his obsession with death and carnal desire, did I identify that precise smell of tuberose which had so often turned my stomach. "When tuberoses are rotting," he says in *Nana*, "they have the smell of the human body."

All human beings past their youth struck me as giving off this whiff of mortal decay. Yet my own parents were young and beautiful, full of high spirits, with a horror of the "children of old people." In our chitchat the girls would bring up the age of their parents. The younger the better. Poor Baudelaire! Part of the fragrance of *Les fleurs du mal* is no doubt a compensation for his father's advanced age.

In Baudelaire's "banned poems" we had discovered, at the age of fifteen, the existence of Lesbians. The key poem was *Delphine et Hippolyte*. Danielle, brave girl, had made copies of it on her father's typewriter. Baudelaire did not circulate freely at that time. Never was a poem so carefully picked over. Every word was weighed, analysed. The love of literature is never unmixed. Students who rebel against elaborate attempts to explain the text by isolating the "beauties" are able, when really moved by the subject, to reproduce perfectly the niggling pedantry of teachers of the "old school." So it was with us.

Every word was sifted and screened. "But Hippolyte is a man's name!" I cried. We consulted Larousse. Poor Larousse, shamelessly exploited to satisfy our insatiable sexual curiosity: no, it was our "attachment to scientific truth," one of us would insist. Larousse, à la Machiavelli, defended itself with adult ruses, leading us on from Charybdis to Scylla. But Danielle triumphed. Larousse had not foreseen the final *coup* and drily announced the existence of a certain Hippolyta, "Queen of the Amazons, in Scythia, conquered by Hercules." So, it was true.

Once the question was settled, we hastened to forget it. A certain uneasiness weighed on our little band of girls. We hardly dared link arms now, make friendly or familiar gestures. In case it might lead to "that." Danielle realized her mistake. She had meant to show us "what was what," to thwart "those darned sisters" with their obsession with sin. We became still more alarmed. Hadn't Baudelaire himself used that word "concupiscent" which used to make us burst with merriment every time the sisters

46

trotted it out? And the punishment he had foretold for us, of feeling "our flesh flap like an old flag," seemed quite severe, coming from a layman.

This line of the poem made little impression on me. Nobody *had* to indulge in this forbidden pleasure, which was moreover so carefully concealed that its very existence had so far escaped us. But then weren't we "condemned" to a "stupid *fiancé*," with the added punishment of bringing him a pair of "stigmatised breasts"? This circumstance of physical love, as conceived by man and described by Baudelaire, plunged me into amazement and revulsion. I had discovered that this was the symptom by which women first revealed the encroachments of old age. Those flaccid breasts, soft and heavy, men wickedly made them the attributes of the women they "loved." Horror! I, who had so dearly wished to "have" them. This was my punishment.

37

Such were the follies that occupied me during those years. I might have taken fine mystic flights. I did not. The religious nonsense so copiously retailed by the sisters and *curés* ruled that out. Every stage in a woman's life has no doubt its own miseries. I dragged my own adolescence behind me for so long, took so many years to emerge from its hard shell, that now I'm refusing the ordeal of the menopause, that other burden of ungrateful age.

I have seldom been physically "well adjusted." First that long childhood, and then the interminable adolescence when I kept twisting and turning in a frantic attempt to transform myself. There is a great deal of talk these days of the right to life, to health, to happiness. What about the right to beauty? It was denied me. A revolting act of injustice. The hungry man, faint with desire before the shop-window crammed with food, dreams that some day he'll be rich and eating his fill, or that he'll break the window and seize the things he craves. But how can I seize beauty? Throughout those foolish years everything confirmed me in the idiotic notion that beauty was the only passport to love.

38

You found me beautiful. You told me so. I never believed you. At that time it made no difference to me whether you did or not. I thought all that mattered was the warm conspiracy of our bodies rejoicing in each other.

39

Bodies are swift to age. My parents watched with dismay the first crumbling of their physical perfection. A certain thickening of contours, and hair growing thin and brittle. It is now my turn to endure that dreadful moment when a woman is no longer a woman but "of a certain age." Wrinkles underscore her features which, like concrete, have already set. At the same time her other outlines merge. The curve of the back, neck and loins is blurred. Breasts turn to chests, hips to laps. The *shape* disappears. Instead of forms, masses. Colours become vague hues; the beiges and greys take over; the frightful blueish tints of English and German tourists with their varieties of steel-grey hair—all this is the prescribed uniform of those who have ceased to live.

I still fight back. Alone, disdained, despised, left on the shelf, I still use the old recipes. Strict diet, friction

48

glove, creams, ointments. Brushing my hair, plucking my eyebrows, and all the rest of it. Yet it's not my body you despise. You used to like it well enough. It's my soul, stubborn, wilful and fiercely bent on being acknowledged, that you have rejected.

40

I hesitate to begin this chapter. There was, after all, a moment in my life when I suffered more than now. I did not weep then, any more than I do now. I took the blow right in my heart. Sudden, brutal, irrevocable. For days I refused to accept its message.

"Weep, my dear. It will help," Danielle implored me. I could not.

Misfortune always knocks when least expected. This time also I opened my door to it. A policeman. Unhappy, ill at ease. Full of sympathy and circumlocution. He told me my parents were dead. Both of them, together. On that Laurentian highway they used to take to go skiing. I hardly heard him describing the icy road, the truck. I only wanted him to stop talking. To go away. He insisted on my not staying in the house; he telephoned Danielle, informed her parents. I was beset on all sides. Horrible ceremonies, apparently indispensable, had to be gone through.

41

I had no desire to look at them again, knowing how they would have hated me to preserve such a lying image of them, with their faces made up with the macabre artistry of the undertaker's men. I refused to shed tears, to sleep, eat, wash. I was in fact refusing reality. They had abandoned me. An orphan. The word fell on me like a club, with its message of unpardonable betrayal. When the pain attacked my chest, hindering my breathing, I tore my hair.

42

The service in the church. I would like to have wept, but only for the injustice of this pair of deaths. They had worshipped life. They had travelled so far from their native land only not to lose a single day of it. They never spoke of death or illness. "One must believe in happiness." And they had believed in it. This life which I so feared, they were in love with it. I would gladly have changed places with them.

43

The cemetery. A fine soft snow had begun to fall. The coffins were lowered. First one, then the other. My mother first. Then my father, as if to shield her with his body for the last time. At last I wept. I realized they had abandoned me once again. They had remained together in death and left me, alone and inconsolable, behind.

44

During the few nights when we slept together, I often thought of killing myself. You were always soon asleep. I could easily have risen and swallowed the score of sleeping pills I always kept with me. I would have fallen asleep forever in your arms instead of dying alone, like a dog. But

I took pity on your imagined awakening, your panic. That is why I am here, still struggling in this nightmare.

45

At that time I was also struggling. Danielle's parents were kindness itself. I stayed with them for months. They helped me dispose of the apartment and sell off the furniture. There was also still a little money in the bank. The remains of their famous "capital."

"If you're careful you can make it last till you finish high school."

I decided to be "careful."

46

I got through my final year in school in a kind of daze.

"There's no harm in trying," Danielle's parents had kept urging. With angelic patience Danielle herself saw me through my year. My apprenticeship in learning things by heart, imposed on me by the "good sisters," enabled me to repeat everything as faultlessly as a parrot. I slid through my examinations like a sleepwalker.

47

That summer the war was won. The flags flew. I was filled with a boundless sadness as I faced a world at peace, a world where I myself could find no place.

Ingenuous as I was, unused to any kind of introspection, I yet realized my grief was not pure but mixed with anger and bitterness.

They had left me in the lurch.

"Shift for yourself."

They themselves had managed to make their exit. Together, in the midsummer splendour of their love. But the war was over, that war whose sufferings they had so dreaded—and they were dead.

As for me, I missed my own cue to exit. I waited too long. I shall die alone, in the folding-in of an autumn I no longer dare to face. I should have arranged to leave the stage in my eighteenth year. The rest of my life has been nothing but an absurd process of marking time.

With the end of hostilities I at last grasped what this abominable war had accomplished. Europe in ruins. Persecutions, trials. The shock of these horrors threw me into confusion. My years of self-imposed blindness had cost me dear. With growing fascination I read about the concentration camps and gas chambers in Silesia and Poland.

We had heard in 1940 of my grandmother's death after a short illness. This was the only time my grandfather communicated with us. "In deference to your mother's last wishes," he wrote. No one told us of his own death. I had inquiries made. He had been picked up in one of the first Paris round-ups. I never learned anything more. This bereavement was now added to the others. The death of this unknown man seemed at times to cause me more suffering than any of them.

51

The strange sense of guilt. I was afflicted by the idea of living on the proceeds of a transaction paid for by six million dead. I blamed my parents. We ought to have stayed on, with the others, sharing the common lot. One has no right to run away. I wished to be one of the victims. My parents had refused me this communion of sacrifice. And they themselves had fled to no purpose. Death had caught up with them, in spite of everything. Their ending was meaningless, like my life.

52

I went back to school for my senior matriculation in the fall. They gave me "special rates," and in return I gave French lessons to some of the smaller English girls. Outwardly I was tractable. I had only a year to "kill" before my matriculation.

Throughout the war the good sisters had maintained a prudent silence. As soon as it was over there was an orgy of thanksgiving to celebrate the Return of Peace. One day I took them to task.

"We should have prayed before, against those acts of genocide, shouldn't we? But a few Jews more or less, what difference did that make?"

I was severely reprimanded. I was impertinent. Ungrateful. They would excuse me on compassionate grounds, since my recent bereavement had no doubt "upset" me. Provided I made an apology. I did so. It did not cost me too much. I knew I had been unjust. Like my own parents trying to persuade themselves their sacrifice had been made for my sake. This remorse, this monstrous mental blindness, could not be charged to the sisters but to myself. I had tried to make them share the burden of a transgression too heavy for me to bear alone. So, without too much hypocrisy, I apologized to Mother Superior for my scandalous remark.

53

I could hardly wait to leave them. To hear no more those dry voices, those platitudes, that twaddle retailed with such unfailing assurance. In my simplicity, I thought everything would be different at the university.

54

Once again I made the effort "to make trial of life." If I am to kill myself some day soon it will not be for want of trying to overcome my taste for annihilation, this constantly renewed temptation to be swallowed in the matrix of death.

I had figured carefully. I had still enough money to last the two years required to take my degree in arts. Danielle's parents kept telling me, "That's hardly practical just now. Wait." They tried to steer me into social work or dietetics. But I wanted to enjoy some respite in the only oasis I could see.

55

I stood firm. I registered at the Université de Montréal. Danielle was just beginning her own course in medicine there: our paths were diverging. In those closing years of the forties the Arts Faculty had almost no students but the "Washouts," as they were called. This was a comfort. I would be among my own kind, without having to play a part.

With three other girls I found an apartment. Two of them came from Abitibi, the other from Sherbrooke. I shared the largest bedroom with the Sherbrooke girl; the two others, who had moved in first, had each a small one to herself. There was a big living room and a huge kitchen where we sometimes took our meals together. This way of living suited me. I enjoyed companionship as well as the independence of living in an apartment rather than in a room under the surveillance of a "family." I liked to hear the girls chattering and teasing each other. They greeted me pleasantly, morning and evening. We took turns doing the housework and the cooking.

56

My first experience of the university was disappointing. The lecture rooms were just like those in school. And the first row of seats was of course graced by an assortment of "black cattle." For there sat the sisters, always blocking the view with their immense white-winged coifs, and the Brothers of the Christian Schools with those blue bibs which made them look like dazed and retarded infants, plus a few "fathers" in their shiny cassocks. The holy family, in full strength. They made up the bulk of the squad. Though the word was not yet fashionable, they were in fact "recycling" themselves at that propitious period. Grimly determined to have and to hold forever the fief of education as their exclusive preserve. When they graduated, positions awaited them in the regional schools throughout the province. As for us, when our studies were finished we were faced with either unemployment or some kind of menial quill-driving. They had cornered everything! The lay students, much less in number, who had chosen this faculty had done so at their own risk and peril, with full knowledge of what they were in for. "For the love of art." Our teachers were also drawn from the priestly caste, and the few laymen on duty were still more fiercely "clerical." Before every lecture a prayer in Latin was delivered, though the genuine clergy sometimes spared us this.

My fellow students were in revolt, but discreetly. This was no time of militant demands. We groused among ourselves. The boys claimed it was "worse than school."

"The Jesuits at least have more style to them. We had some who were really quite bright."

I said nothing. Personally, I preferred the university. Here the sisters themselves were back in school, being "instructed" along with us—it was their turn now! —instead of making us devour the prescribed text-books. And even though all the important authors weren't on the reading list their number was less restricted than in convent. True, there were some strange gaps. The whole eighteenth century was passed over in silence. But, knowing nothing, I determined to learn as much as I could—and perhaps finish my education later on.

You see, I've always been "reasonable." Ready to adjust my grasp to the smallest portion of life within my reach. A little air to breathe, a few drops of water for refreshment.

The "clever" ones scoffed at our new masters, claiming they were simply repeating, word for word, the learned works which they frankly believed no one had heard of but themselves. Ignorant of these famous sources on which they drew, I enjoyed listening to men "in the prime of life" speaking with enthusiasm on subjects that enthralled me.

In this sphere I was happy. I ought never to have "taken my nose out of my books," as I had been forced to do at the age of ten. Here I was at ease, sheltered, tasting the imaginary joys of passion instead of enduring the heartbreak of waiting and frustration. I ought to have kept this refuge. My only periods of "happiness" have been passed with beings who never lived. Or in trying to create others on paper.

57

As for the courses, I got through them pleasantly enough. The famous Lectures struck me as little more than so many excuses for reverie. I simply went wool-gathering in the intervals between quotations. From time to time a line or passage of poetry would capture my attention, for the professors didn't talk all the time and sometimes had the good taste to interpolate a fine or moving passage, often quite well delivered. I was satisfied with what I got.

There was also recess. We of the laity had formed a kind of mafia made up of the students who had chosen that most unsaleable of commodities, "pure" literature. Whether French, English or American made little difference to us, as long as it was "literature."

"You've nothing in common with them," Danielle declared. In her eyes we were dirty, slovenly, and pretentious to boot. "Lazy idle snobs. You don't *do* a damn thing. The world just doesn't interest you. Always with your heads in the clouds."

It was true. We took no part in "university activities," in the rallies, meetings and charity bazaars on which she doted. In her set, they stuck to their books but also kept "up to date," dressed to the nines in navy-blue blazers with the university crest, spotless grey skirts or slacks and dazzling white blouses or shirts. While we lounged about in old sweaters and filthy shapeless raincoats. This was our get-up. I wore it with pride.

"I've been in uniform quite long enough."

Faithful to our old friendship and determined not to let me "fall," Danielle tried to make me see the light. No argument came amiss. She even invoked the maternal shades. "Your mother, so elegant. . . . If she could see you now, looking like a tramp."

My mother would certainly have loaded me with advice on elegance or at least on "common decency." I redoubled my efforts to find costumes still more uncouth. It was my revenge on the years I had spent trying to be pretty. In my set, the worse you dressed the better you looked.

For hours on end we would argue in the university canteen, swapping titles of recent books. Whether freshmen or sophomores, we were the nuttiest lot on the campus.

Yet we were desperately "proper." Our only extravagances were verbal. We got high on words. The boys drank very little, the girls did not "sleep around." No question of drugs: we hadn't even money to buy cigarettes! As for books, we borrowed them from the public libraries every week.

We were serious kids. And studious too, whatever
Danielle might think. We spent hours in the university
library, that huge reverberating railway concourse with
its shelves so sparsely furnished with modern authors.

We were just discovering Sartre. For our excursions
we got ourselves up in hideous clothes which were, for us,
the height of existentialist sophistication. We talked of
nothing but *engagement*, unconscious of any need for
action. Somewhere in the provincial hinterland the mi-
ners were fighting Duplessis' police. On our hilltop we
saw ourselves as the paladins of free speech whenever we
managed to get an article on Gide, Sartre or Balzac
printed in the *Quartier Latin*.

I don't regret those years. Considering our helplessness,
we could have done nothing more towards "liberating"
ourselves. Since the war, this word *liberation* was always
on our lips. I knew *Huis Clos* by heart. Ingenuously I
would repeat, *L'enfer c'est les autres.* Never suspecting
that hell is within oneself, and that whether one is twenty,
thirty or forty, not to live with or for another is one's own
portion of it.

There were those parties in the slums. In the east end of
town, where the drinks were cheaper. We made a scotch
or a coke last the whole evening. Sometimes we would
organize an excursion to the country. No, we weren't a

spoiled generation. We were delighted with little things. We would save up for weeks to have a picnic on some lake or other. The girls furnished the food, the boys the transportation. When we went off for a week-end, we shared the rent.

"Nothing is 'going on'," I assured Danielle, who would laugh. Far from admiring our virtue, she found us "peculiar." And instead of applying the word "virtuous" to our continence, she spoke of "fear" and "complexes." In my own case, she was not far wrong. Yet partnerships were in fact formed among us. Like that of Louise and Gérard, holding hands, murmuring secrets in the corridors and lecture-rooms. Others had found "without the walls" the partner of their dreams, the ideal friend. Of the original mafia only a little knot of the faithful remained. Alain, Guy and Roméo ("their very names were predestined," Danielle laughed), Gaétane and myself. Danielle suspected them of the worst depravities, declaring she had "put me wise" in vain when I was fifteen, if I still didn't know what they "were after."

Her own outings were of a "serious" nature. With a law student in his third year, "one of the top men in his class." She and I had now little in common. Yet our early friendship prevented any final break. Her parents liked me. They continued to invite me to their home on Sundays. In summer they pressed me to spend part of my holidays at their country place in the Eastern Townships. This was my only contact with "normal life." And I clung to it. The Guillaumes were lecturing me "only for my own good." I was grateful. All the same, I was stubbornly bent on going my own way.

61

And yet I was "doing" nothing. Getting nowhere. They reproached me for my idleness.

"But I'm working. I've passed my first year's exams."

Such ingenuousness shocked them.

"But after that?"

"I'll go to work."

Madame Guillaume, like Danielle herself, wanted me to listen to reason.

"You spend too much time alone. You ought to get married, fall in love with some nice boy."

These conversations depressed me. For weeks on end. I had no desire for a nice boy, and I was not "in love" with anyone.

"Your little friends are conning you," Danielle insisted. "They find you all right for some crummy evening, but when they go out in a big way they take someone else."

I knew what she meant. I had already been shaken to find that Alain and Guy had gone to the university Prom. For this memorable event they had taken two dieticians. Haughty and elegant, these girls laughed their heads off at "literature." The boys had scraped up the price of the tickets—ten dollars a couple—not counting the obligatory floral *corsage.* They often used to borrow money from me when they were short. I was a little surprised by the sum they laid out for such a silly occasion. Gaétane and I were left high and dry.

62

I had not been "asked." I was hurt, upset.

"I didn't have a dress."

"I'd have lent you one," said Danielle. "Come on, admit it. You weren't asked."

I lied.

"Oh yes, Roméo asked me."

Even today I still don't know why I felt I had to deceive my only friend. She said nothing more. On the spur of the moment, I had told this lie out of simple politeness. Nothing in the world would have made me wear an old dress to my first dance.

63

There were no dances for me that winter. Nor the following winters. I pretended indifference, giving my mourning as excuse. You too, you never asked me to a dance. Even today this memory pains me.

64

It was not so much the dances themselves. But I would have liked to go, to see what they were really like. After all those descriptions in novels, pictures, movies, I'd have liked to compare them. It was a shock to find I was "beyond the pale." I was all right to talk to, as a comrade. To receive confidences. Now I saw that even for these literary types the world of books ran second. It was stupid of me not to see it before. For them too, literature was not "real life." This disappointment was a good lesson to me. Instead of wasting my time reading, I decided to think of the future.

65

I made this "realistic" resolve one Saturday evening, in the empty apartment. I was swept as if by a tidal wave. The three girls had gone out. They were going out more and more. Colette and Françoise had their regular boy friends. Brigitte played the field and was never at home. Mechanically, I finished tidying up. Then I picked up the telephone. I called Danielle. She was out. Madame Guillaume took over. "All on your lonesome, on a Saturday night? Come on over, if you want to. We're playing bridge tonight. There's plenty of nice little biscuits. . . ." I thanked her as politely as I could. One after another I called Roméo, Alain, Guy. None of them was free. At last I called Gaétane. I knew I was no siren, but Gaétane's looks had always reassured me about my own. She was a big husky girl with a deep voice, huge feet and those enormous circular hornrimmed spectacles which were not fashionable at that time. This policemanlike appearance had confirmed Danielle in her verdict on the girl. Gaétane was not "right." I was doing myself no manner of good by being seen everywhere with her.

"You look like a real married couple, the two of you. It's enough to scare the boys off."

Whenever she was feeling "out of sorts" Gaétane would telephone me. I had never refused to keep her company or listen to her analysing herself. This time I would have liked to reverse the roles. But Gaétane had "someone" with her. She announced the fact with pride. I persisted. She appeared not to understand and simply hung up saying, "So long for now."

So when she had "someone" with her, Gaétane didn't give a hoot for her girl friends. Far from sharing Danielle's suspicions, I was quite sure that the mere presence of a boy had made her drop me like a hot potato. I was not

mistaken. She got married soon after, to her "someone."
He was a dentist, with spectacles as big as her own.

66

A real rash of marriages was breaking out. Christmas
fiancées became June brides. Unattached girls were few
and far between. I understood the strictures of the Guillaumes.

"The longer you wait, playing hard to get, the harder
it will be. . . ." They forbore to add, "to get married." I
knew what they were thinking. A kind of dizziness seized
me. Far from playing "hard to get," the smallest success
would have braced me. Any attention, the slightest compliment. But whenever it was a question of getting me
"suited" I somehow reverted to my infantile awkwardness. "You do it on purpose," Danielle told me.

Out of the goodness of her heart she had tried to
arrange evening foursomes, when her own fiancé would
drag along some friend of his. These were called *blind
dates*. Even if my luckless partner for the evening had
been really blind he could not have been deaf as well. I
had always been complimented on my voice. The scarcity
of my good points, compared to those of other girls, was
presumably redressed by this vocal attraction.

"You are charming, with that Parisian accent,"
Madame Guillaume would say, trying to cheer me up.

But on these parties, without doing anything "on purpose" but only out of sheer nervousness, I would hear this
Parisian voice of mine rising to a shriek. I would make
faces, laugh in the wrong places, and misinterpret the
innocent jokes which half the time I didn't understand
—simply from some perverse obsession to find in them
the double meanings that I actually found revolting.

As well as these "arranged" evenings, there were the big parties Danielle gave in her basement. I was just as miserable at these. To escape notice I would busy myself rinsing the glasses in the kitchen with Madame Guillaume; and I would go round with the trays of cakes and sandwiches, passing them three times instead of once. The guests must have taken me for the maid, for the kind of hired girl who always overdoes things.

I stopped going to these parties where I was so miserable. That was the year when you yourself often went to Danielle's. You were finishing your course in medicine. She found you brilliant. If I hadn't been such a fool I would have met you ten years earlier. But it would have changed nothing, I know. At that time you liked beautiful, smashing girls. The wife you picked proves it. You wouldn't have even looked at me, much less asked me to dance while I was passing trays and trying to attract as little attention as possible.

Michel was the first man I met on my own. Right away, he fascinated me. Not handsome, but he seemed to stand out in this drab lecture-room setting. His very dress was like a disguise. He had a strange, tormented expression. Astonishingly mobile features. I could follow his reactions to the lectures and tell at once whether he approved or not.

In the front rows sat the religious orders. The rest of us

occupied the back benches. He sat by himself at a window, as if in deliberate isolation. No one dared sit beside him. I studied him, watching his expression. Everything seemed to affect him. I saw that a mounting number of small details were putting him in a rage: I listened, trying to gauge his final reaction. One day, engrossed by a lecture on the Middle Ages, I forgot to keep watch on him. All at once he got up, very pale, looked the professor up and down and left, slamming the door behind him. I tried to find out what had unleashed this violence, but in vain. I told myself I would solve the mystery. At the next lecture luck was with me. My usual place was taken. I hesitated, then sat down beside him. This obviously annoyed him. I did not speak. He appeared to dismiss me from his thoughts. He was taking notes with a kind of frantic care. Despite my shyness and my dread of seeming "forward," I took note of his bizarre hand-writing. A curious scrawl with all the letters squeezed together, very thick and tall, without any spacing or the slightest margin. There was something sickly and disturbing about it.

70

Then he spoke to me. Not that day, but after another lecture on the Middle Ages. He had missed some of the preceding ones. When it was over he turned to me:

"What do you think of Dionne?"

I decided to play it straight. "He's our best teacher."

He seemed to reflect.

"Yes," he said. "And he trades on it."

He refused to elaborate.

71

"I've studied for the priesthood," he told me. Point blank. "You're surprised?"

I was not. I saw now why he had seemed "disguised" in civilian clothes. Everything was clear. A man set apart. Neither one of "us," nor one of the others. He asked me if I could be discreet. I assured him I could. His mind set at rest, he proposed a meeting. I accepted eagerly.

72

My meetings with Michel took place in the oddest places, in outlandish parts of town where I had never been before. It was some time before I understood he didn't want to be seen by anyone he knew. Stupidly, I had at first been flattered by the pains he took in choosing such mysteriously romantic places for our outings. We would walk together through the rain and sleet, always at top speed. I would lose my breath trying to keep up with him, as I used to with my parents long ago.

"You won't tell anyone about our meetings?"

I promised not to. Quite apart from my pledged word, common prudence would have restrained me. Danielle would have hit the roof. My own set would have accused me of "treating with the enemy." And even if Michel no longer wore the cassock—*"they wouldn't have me"*—he was only planning how to re-assume it. He often disappeared to Saint-Benoît or some other monastery.

I had hoped to make him talk. But it was he who "confessed" *me*. With a kind of hunger. To please him I would invent scruples, doubts and "spiritual" leanings which I was far from feeling. He took me to masses, vespers, interminable recitations of the rosary. He would glare at me whenever I yawned. To gratify him, I feigned fervour. Gradually these "walks" assumed a singular importance in my life.

He exploited his power over me. When I tried to throw off his influence, he took unfair advantage. Instead of arguing he would take me abruptly by the hand, without uttering a word. I was so innocent that this contact disturbed me. I trembled. With trepidation, with delight, my palms moist, my heart pounding. He would release me just as abruptly. As if it had meant nothing. Without seeming to notice my feelings, my wild excitement. Then he would revert to my "vocation."

One day I exclaimed in a fury, "I've never been a believer! You know it. I've told you." He brushed this aside, calmly affirming that those who defend themselves most fiercely are already won over. Then I understood. My "conversion" would prove he had the gift of bringing lost sheep back to the fold. I was choking with indignation. Little by little I had revealed my true situation to him, my frightful feelings of guilt. And he turned them to his own account. Since I felt guilty, I had only to "atone" by a life of pious sacrifice. When he held forth blithely on the beauties of the New Testament, without understanding or trying to put himself in my place, he filled me with horror. I despised him for the blindness which spared him any qualms over the indignity of such a religious "deal." The little Jewish part of me, shameful, denied, hidden, was now to be redeemed through the dawning of a bright Christian conscience. Indeed.

"You want me to cheat?"

When I left school I had vowed to drop all religious observances. I had kept my word. Easter was approaching. Michel must have had only one end in view: to make me take Holy Communion. He was showing himself more bigoted than the good sisters themselves. They had no inkling of one's reservations and reluctancies. They were at least ingenuous.

Michel's motives were not innocent. He had an odd way of combining the sacred with the profane. He dangled the bait of this Holy Week before me, conjoining the joys of religion with certain others. He suggested that I leave Montreal. At Oka, there was this lake; and the monastery. To cap our week-end together, the Sunday of the Resurrection.

"I should so like to approach the Lord's Table with you."

I could take it or leave it. This wasn't stated explicitly. It's only in books, in those implacable tragedies à la Corneille, that everything is set forth clearly, in alexandrines.

An older, more sophisticated girl would have laughed in his face. And perhaps have cured him. I remained in torment for days, keeping my promise to say nothing to anyone. Occasionally he returned to the attack.

"What about our plan?"

If I refused I would lose him for good. I knew it.

At twenty one is stupider than at forty. One is also stronger. More straightforward.

"I'm sorry, it's impossible."

"You are disappointing me, terribly. . . ."

He repeated this two or three times.

At twenty one is also more unkind. When *you* broke with me I didn't tell you a few home truths touching your cowardice and want of principle. In my triumph at having found Michel out, I threw this in his teeth: "The Jesuits were right not to take you. You would have made a bad priest."

I had undergone this "trial." And kept my little "soul"
intact. I've had no luck in my choice of men. You wanted
none of my soul, and he wanted none of my body. The
only man with whom I tried to "make a life" wanted
neither. That's another story: I'm coming to it. But before
consigning the episode of Michel to oblivion I must confess to you that, in the matter of the only "safe" places for
our own meetings, he had finally left it up to me to find
them. Which only goes to show that everything has its
use, as Claudel would say!

74

Michel never spoke to me again. The college year drew to
its end. He didn't take his examinations. I on the other
hand had vowed to excel in this field. I composed my
theses in a burst of energy and with an over-mastering
desire to shine. The results surpassed my expectations. I
even bragged a little.

"That's not the way to make yourself popular,"
Danielle told me. Once again she was right. Even my own
little group gave me the cold shoulder.

75

Twenty is no longer the "golden age." Today, however,
when I am twice that age, I am dismayed to find that I
suffer twice—no, ten times—as much from certain afflic-
tions. I forgot Michel soon enough. After a few weeks I
had quite recovered. The wound had scarred over, leaving no mark. A mistake, a passing accident. I might even

have taken the initiative, in my turn. And it was no more than a few months before I accepted the fact that the "story" was definitely over. I simply made the best of a bad job, I suppose. Today I am so drained, so deeply wounded that I'm summoning up from the past everything that can help me to obliterate, if only for a second or two, the one sorrow that matters, the one pain that is spreading and covering my whole life like a monstrous oil slick.

76

I try in vain to overlook the barbarity of this silence of yours. You will make no move, give me no cause for hope. The summer will end on this note of bankruptcy. Like those besotted romantic heroes who used to blow their brains out over some point of honour, I will not survive the loss of my faith in you. This summer's end is my deadline, when I'll write *finis* to these hollow days, these fruitless hours.

77

Foolishly, I hoped the past would help me see things clearly. I was wrong. Far from helping me to endure it, the sad chronicle of those days only confirms the pitiless verdict. The good hardworking student will be failed in the only examination that matters to her, thrown back into the limbo of non-existence.

78

What with one thing and another, my life's at a discount. Soiled merchandise. I'm ready to sell off what's left of it. But who wants the remnants of a ruined life? Telling over each sad episode, I see they are all strung together. One imitation pearl after another. What a cheap necklace you're wearing, madam.

79

It's my own. I've strung it, day after day, night after night. Imitation pearls, neither pink nor white. Not even black. A uniform grey, leaden and lustreless.

80

Here I am, halfway through my task. I've already re-strung half of these glass beads which are my stock in trade. I've still a month of life left. Twenty more years to "add." Once the last row is finished, the last knot tied, I'll bite off the thread. And I'm not going to burn in hell. I'm there already.

81

Life was none too easy in 1950; but the students managed to "place" themselves for the summer holidays, as long as they planned well ahead and weren't too choosy about the jobs offered them. If they saved their wages they could pay the fees for the coming year. That summer I went to work for the first time in my life, proud of being able to earn my living at last. I hadn't found the pleasantest or the most lucrative kind of job. Some of the girls went to Banff as waitresses. As well as the free trip, they raked in "fantastic sums" in tips. I had found a job that I thought quite enviable. At Morgan's Department Store, behind the souvenir counter specially designed for passing tourists, for those old American ladies enraptured by the beauty of our native handicrafts. They bought an incredible quantity of hideous objects, clucking joyfully. Then there was the wrapping, the mailing, and working out the difference between our dollars and theirs. Noticing my awkwardness, my obvious mistakes, they would say, "It's your first day here, isn't it, dear?" I would say it was. They were more than happy to help me; they added up the bills, lent a hand tying the parcels. I was delighted to wash up on this peaceful shore. My fellow salesladies at the busier counters met interesting people and made bigger commissions. I was glad to be forgotten in my little corner. In off hours, on the sly, I used to read—though this was strictly forbidden.

82

It was a hot summer, and I was glad to see it end. I was looking forward to the new college term. I had saved up during the summer, and ventured to treat myself to an expensive tailored suit. And I went to a "smart" hairdresser who cut my hair short. I thought I was transformed. No one paid any attention to my "metamorphosis." I took this as a lesson: from now on, I wouldn't squander money on things that no one noticed.

I'm exaggerating. Claude Guichard noticed everything. I've not yet mentioned him. He wasn't one of our set, but kept shifting from one faculty to another, year after year: now in arts, now in psychology, now in philosophy. The Eternal Student, they called him. Ten years older than any of us, he even had a few grey hairs: he also had wealthy parents who were growing tired of his want of direction. The girls went into raptures over his "charm." The boys snickered—at least the ones who liked girls did so; the others found him much to their taste, no doubt. Claude took pains to keep up his reputation as a lady-killer. He went out with all the highly rated or "new" girls—once at least, sometimes oftener. But he soon dropped them. Instinctively Danielle detested him, without guessing what he "was." Her naiveté amused me, and I was pleased with my own acumen.

I had in fact discovered Claude's secret. On our first evening out I was relieved and reassured: he at least wasn't trying to "get me off in a corner," like all the rest. But I was mistaken. He began "forcing" his attentions, so as not to show his true colours. I drew away from him: "You don't have to play games with me." At first he took my "scorn" in bad part. I tried to make him see that I liked him just as he was. He didn't come clean all at once. He kept telling me long stories about his unhappy love affairs. So many lovely Swedish girls, so many enigmatic Greek ones—they had all made him suffer. I let him talk. At that time I had read Proust, with no illusions about the sex of Albertine. I used the same code for Claude's stories. Little by little he revealed his real tastes.

We became friends. I found him handsome and brilliant. "I know all about you now," he told me. "You're as

silent as the tomb." He pretended to believe I also had my
"secrets." He was tired of wearing a mask. I gave him
some respite from deceit.

We often went out together. Thanks to Claude,
everyone knew about it. I was glad to cease being Cin-
derella. It was now my turn to brag of smart evening
engagements. On Saturday nights I was "busy," like other
girls. The Guillaumes were delighted. Danielle alone
would not concur. "He's wasting your time. He'll never
marry anyone. It's not his bag."

I closed off this kind of talk. Even to her I dared not
admit my fear of marriage, of any binding contract.

Claude was really kind. He lent me books, took me to
the theatre and concerts. He declared I had style, "class."
A pretty voice, with a "ravishing" accent. Of course he
was looking for excuses for taking out such a commonplace
girl. When he was in high good humour he called me
"Princess." I was under his spell.

84

He could be extremely charming when he took the trouble. I frankly admired his mastery of the piano, his knowledge of Khmer art and Byzantine civilization. I listened to
him, quite carried away. Now and then I would ask a
question. This would set him off again. I admired him
more than ever, idiot that I was.

85

I'm amazed now by that passion. It's only normal to be a
little silly at that age: for some girls it's their greatest

charm, but if I mean to be honest here I must go deeper. I must recognize, in myself, the falsity I condemn in others.

86

For I was not such a fool. I saw through Claude. And I said nothing. I was relieved to find someone as fantastic as myself. He was playing a part, and I was glad to play opposite him in this bad drawing-room comedy.

87

Today, I am struck by the absurdity of that burlesque. My girl friends, whom I was trying to imitate slavishly, were goody-goody types, genuine *oies blanches*. I myself was just a goose.

88

Goose or pigeon, the particular bird in such a barnyard doesn't matter. They all end up in the kitchen, in the oven. Eventually I was to become "the pigeon" in this foolish confidence game we played for the benefit of other people.

89

The past is over and done with. I have no right to harry this dead self of mine, my sister of yesterday. I was stupid.

Why deny it? Why blame myself? We can't change our
spots.

90

So I played my spurious part, and Claude played his. He
had good reason for this mummery. His parents would
have stopped his allowance if they had "suspected." The
thought of the shock to his mother and father terrified
him.

"They hardly know such 'horrors' exist."

So he spared them, by avoiding confrontations. He
was also protecting his casual "sweethearts." For he had
several. As for me, I was of no interest to anyone. In the
eyes of my girl friends, Claude and I were just another
couple.

91

I was foolishly glad to be part of this entity entitled
"Hélène and Claude" by my friends, and "Claude and
Hélène" by his. To pull the wool over people's eyes, the
way it's done in stories and novels, gave me a strange
sense of satisfaction. That was the height of my ambition
in my twenties!

92

It has always given me a slight surprise to see my shadow
on a wall or on the ground. So I had a shadow. And
fingerprints too, uniquely mine. Even today I'm not con-

vinced of the reality of my life or the possibility of my death. I'm trying to pin them both down, to trap them on these sheets of paper. Once I've carefully described the various stages leading to this necessary, inevitable suicide of mine, I'll go ahead with it. It's the only solution. By ceasing to exist I will have made my first genuine choice as a living person. Exit Hélène.

93

Yes, I was christened Hélène. I've covered all these pages before admitting it. An Hélène should be beautiful. I was not. Plenty of girls have names that don't suit them, and they carry on all the same. But I am crushed by everything.

94

The only beings I have ever succeeded in understanding, in loving, have been the characters in novels. Not the people one meets! In everyday life men always seemed to me alarmingly big and heavy. They breathed a massive self-confidence. Their conviction of being useful—and even necessary—to society was unshakeable. All the "nice" boys whom Madame Guillaume dreamed of as possible husbands for me fell into this category. I suspected them of being capable of the worst vulgarities. After a few months of marriage they would be patting me on the behind when introducing me: "my wife." They would beget fine children on me—great big splendid ones, normal in every way. As for myself, one fine day I would find myself normal too, cured, bursting with health.

95

I always yearned for the kind of happiness enjoyed by the majority. But I was the traveller *manquée* who missed the boat and the cruise she dreamed of. Loaded down with parcels, arriving on the dock at the very moment it weighs anchor. It only takes a little courage, a little effort, to run, shout, clamber up the gangway. I remained rooted to the spot. Waving my handkerchief.

96

Meanly, I have envied those women who dared show "what they had" to assume their place in "normal life." For me that life was more thrilling and mysterious than fiction. When my girl friends got married and talked to me of their life, I'd have liked to possess the secret of this transmutation. Their life had an air of truth that all made-up stories lacked. "Nothing" happened there, they claimed. And there, in that "nothing" lay the whole secret. After marriage they became real women, not to be fooled or put upon, displacing their own volume of air, with feet firmly planted on the ground, with hands swift and sure and bearing the blazonry of marriage—and the engagement ring, that chunk of carbon which is the trademark stamped on them once and for all. Claude gave me many rings that were beautiful, odd, exotic. I would rather have deserved the dull conventional band.

97

I was like a child, already convinced I would never grow up when the time came. I watched others going through

the process. I never even began it. Waiting for the Grand
Prize in a lottery where I had no ticket. I would have liked
to change my lot. Some children spend hours licking the
window-panes of candy stores, unable to choose what
they really want. I too know these agonies of indecision.
At the butcher's, for years I couldn't decide between a
steak and a fillet. In a restaurant I always ordered the
same thing. Spaghetti and a cup of coffee. It saved thinking.

98

Claude would scold me for my preposterous eating
habits. When we went out he ordered sensible meals for
both of us. He gave me advice on a horde of subjects. This
was a great comfort. If I try hard enough I'll find he had a
number of good qualities.

99

A sentence of Claude Roy's had always impressed me.
"Exceptional men who have written exceptional books
free us, above all, from our own fear of being exceptional." I never considered myself exceptional, but quite
commonplace. Terrified at being unable to cross the
paper frontier. In books, nothing frightened me. I succeeded in "living" through the medium of print. Yet I
knew the authors of these stories were making up for their
own inability to live them in real life, in a life where
nothing happens, and where there's no need at all to read
or write. At times I would like to be an illiterate. . . .
     But in the world of fiction I can breathe. Discussing
"literature" with my students I do not have to find words,

to talk down to them. It's my world. For good and all. At times I regret this, I feel I'm an old woman, bitter, crazy, sharing her personal drug with defenceless adolescents. For how can we love any creatures of flesh and blood after these marvellous characters fixed forever in their change-less forms? Age cannot stale them, and some words are enshrined in a perpetual youth. I can manage to forget all your rebuffs—as long as I know by heart a few perfect poems that no one can ever take from me. I have still a hundred imaginary universes to explore. And if I don't die I'll go back to Kafka, to Dostoievsky, no longer afraid of finding in them the reflection of my own anguish.

So here I am, free to say whatever I like on these pages. Without you contradicting me. I am suffering less—from the prospect of arranging the end of this story as I wish: after all, I'm the one that decides! I can make you out as inconsolable. As stupid, mean. I'll cut down on my miseries and tortures. If I choose, you'll be ugly, common. You'll have neither awareness nor courage. And I'll make you jealous. I can do anything. I'll get my own back. It's your turn to suffer now. Poor fool, you don't know what's in store for you. You read so little. You sleep so soundly. I'll give you nightmares, remorse, regrets. You'll never see or hear the last of it. Quite simply, without altering a word, I could transcribe your last fright-ful little note here. But that wouldn't be right. There are other ways to pay you out. Ways that go beyond the demands of "realism."

100

It's all a matter of getting one's own back. "Feminine" literature has always been practical, pragmatic, util-itarian. For hundreds of years! I was delighted by some-

81

thing in Simone de Beauvoir's *Mémoires*—when she admits having written *L'Invitée* only to score off a rival.

101

I know what I'm doing. It's not you I'm casting off. Nor any of the people around you. I'm writing these pages simply as a lead-up to the fine ritual murder, the grand symbolic festival when I'll immolate myself in style. I'll kill her, this scabby ewe who spent ten whole years of her life in your shadow, bleating.

102

The altars of my own people have known other victims. Fatted calves and sheep, offered up with all the usual ceremonies to appease a wrathful God. I've found the way out at last. Alive, I'd have run to answer your faintest call. From now on I won't hear you. Too late you'll see the danger of reducing anyone to absolute dependence. Some day the meekest worm will turn, refusing to be stepped on any longer. There are children, it seems, who cannot feel cold, heat or pain. Their lives are in constant danger. That was how I lived for a long time, simply unaware of suffering. Now I'm waking up from this long sleep. I can no longer ignore these insults: to remain the accomplice and partner of certain tortures is unworthy of a human being. The path from slavery to common sense is paved with abjurations. I've decided to take it.

103

The great advantage real love affairs have over "literary" ones has always seemed to lie in their unexpectedness. With each new blow you dealt me, my surprise was so great that it dulled the pain. Like a character in some book I've already read, you no longer surprise me. Before opening your last letter I could foresee the arrangement of its periods to the last comma. The dullest student could have foretold the similarity of this scenario to the ones before. Executioners should be men of some imagination. If not, they're simply butchers, public officials grown grey in their job.

104

All at once I feel young. Lighthearted. Fascinated by the grand role I'm going to play. I love this shift in the *dramatis personae*. The Little Match Girl has become a Fury, thunderbolt in hand. No more those frail fingers blue with cold, that tremulous voice. I'm in charge now: what a surprise! For the first time in ten years. The effect will be all the greater. If I weren't so tired I'd be clapping my hands.

105

Claude was very handsome. Yes he *was*: very, very handsome, I assure you. You'd be bound to agree. Dark flowing locks, the few white hairs only setting them off. Big dark eyes, fringed with amazingly long lashes even on the lower lid. A high forehead. The lower part of the face not quite so good: a nose at once prominent and weak; teeth only so-so, and uneven; a receding chin. Claude knew all his points, good and bad. He improved his profile cleverly. He cultivated beautiful beards, artful moustaches. He dressed superbly well, with everything carefully "harmonized." He taught me a good deal about clothes. For our public appearances I discovered my own style of dressing. My new uniform was a black dress, straight and simple, of the best black velvet, as if I were saying, *this gorgeous man is all the adornment I need.* Like the birds, where the cocks have the fine feathers and the hens the dull ones—that was the kind of pair we made. Everyone accepted it.

The utter cruelty of our society. Only couples are accepted, as in Noah's Ark. Woe betide those who go their own way, by themselves! Claude, older and more experienced, understood this. I was his buckler. He was my shield. We established our partnership tacitly, thrusting away the phantoms that ought to have kept us apart.

106

I must do Danielle justice. She loathed Claude and did her best to pry me loose from him. He returned her dislike. He found her "commonplace, stupid and vulgar." She found him "unbalanced, shifty, affected."

"I can't bear his hands. How can you stand being touched by a man with such revolting hands?" I had never noticed them. "The hands of a murderer," she went on, "the thumbs of a strangler. Just look at them."

I did. It was true. Claude's hands, as carefully looked after as the rest of him, were strangely out of place. Enormous, wide, with spatulate fingers ending in flat nails and disjointed thumbs, with nails bitten to the quick. I was struck by this last feature, so out of place in a man so careful of his appearance. After that, I observed his gestures. He hid his hands as much as possible, keeping the fingers closed.

107

I put my fate into those hands. They were the first hands privileged to explore my body. Up to now I've spoken only of the outward signs and trappings of our affair. There were moments when we were face to face, alone, with no one to deceive, nothing to oblige us to play our parts, no enemy eyes or ears. But the show, the masquerade, went on.

I'd been revolted by the father confessors of my childhood, with their horrible questions, *Where, how, when, how many times?*

Now, when I'm trying to confess the motive of my failure, I see I was never asked the one important question, *Why?* And why did I choose the men who could most surely destroy me?

108

This has been a horrible night, plagued by nightmares. The closer my story draws to the present, the more the cruelty of my experience with you fascinates me. It is not a multiple one: my dreams construct the synthesis. . . . I was a black caterpillar, awaiting her metamorphosis; a little boy, cruel and beautiful, was watching. Suddenly the caterpillar became a butterfly, and the boy seized a green clap-net. I let him catch me, and thought no more of escape. Obediently I fluttered my wings. I was a common yellow butterfly. He proceeded to paint me bright blue. Then, since the paint hindered my movements, he proposed to clip my wings. I let him ply his scissors. But now I flew still more awkwardly. One night I flew away. In the morning I was caught by another boy.

"How strange, it looks like tattooing!"

At first he was very kind. He undertook to cure me, to efface the ugly muddled colours on my wings.

Once more I enjoyed the simplest things. One day, for no reason at all, the little boy decided I had flown enough on my crippled wings. "You're beyond cure," he told me. And with a quick and extraordinarily practised gesture he tore them off. *Doctor Cupid, that was you.*

109

Claude would take me in his arms. I made no resistance. At first he made me endure abominably long sessions of *necking*—an American slang term which is fortunately untranslatable. This "necking" went on before two or three other couples, all similarly engaged. To recover one's breath, one had recourse to watching the others at the same exercise. I despised these games as being a kind of test for the breath-control of a professional diver. The longer the *French kiss* lasted, the higher the marks for the couple's expertise. I quite ruined Claude's reputation. Smothered, I had heavings of the stomach which I desperately tried to camouflage. After these sessions I was nauseated for several hours. But I kept on.

When we were alone Claude gladly dropped this childish game. Then, when there was no audience to watch our manoeuvres, I wanted to resume those tender fondlings. I took the initiative. More or less willingly Claude lent himself to my desires.

"Anyone would think you were trying to be raped," he

would say with a laugh, carefully keeping himself within the allowed limits. "You should be glad you're safe. That's the best thing about boys like me."

His caresses were rough, his movements lacked all tenderness. When he embraced me, his hands on my throat, I thought of Danielle's warning. A slight pressure of his thumbs could have strangled me.

"You're frightened of me," he declared. It was true. But he was frightened too. I could always divine fear in others, unfailingly. He had never "had" a woman: I could have sworn to it. But as usual he continued to lie. He told me fantastic stories of his sexual adventures with beautiful women—amatory experts, fascinating trollops he had met on his travels. He was careful to locate his conquests abroad; his stories had a faint whiff of the Orient Express and Maurice Dekobra. I let him run on. Like a fool, I was dreaming of a miraculous transformation: Claude and I—in love, happy, calm and tender, lost in the peace and unselfishness of mutual affection. My whole heart was fixed on such a relationship. Claude did not care for this at all, and grew impatient. He got even with me in his own way. His caresses grew more unequivocal, and my resistance began to crumble. I wished to be altogether his, to let myself go in his arms, with no thought of anything but pleasure given and received. Claude never "lost control," as he boasted. He would watch me with eyes wide open and a smile of amusement. At the very instant when my desire was reaching its height, he bade me a gracious goodnight.

110

He sent me flowers, splendid bouquets made up with an artistry that my girl friends admired. He took me out to dinner and for walks in the country; he brought me fruit and medicines when I was ill. Colette, Françoise and Brigitte envied me such a gallant cavalier. I said nothing. This comedy lasted a whole year.

111

What was he consciously planning by all this? I had no idea. One day he decided to present me "formally" to his family. He had planned this to get back in his parents' good graces, and to extract money from them. He had decided to obtain his doctorate in France. Up till then he had travelled extensively without doing a stroke of work or getting any kind of degree. His father was not eager to finance any more of these fruitless journeys.

"I'll tell them we're engaged, and that we'll get married when I come back from Europe. They'll be tickled to death. They're wild to have grandchildren."

The idea of conniving in this fraud did not appeal to me at all. I tried to beg off, but finally agreed. Claude rehearsed me carefully, so I would know just what to say and how to say it. He described everything to me, down to the furniture. Strangely enough, I didn't see things the way he did. He was afraid of his father, of his gruffness, his violence. I found the man hearty and animated. For my part, I seemed to surprise him. "You are charming . . . so simple, so delightful." He must have expected some gaudy outlandish creature, and was overjoyed by my banal insignificance. He talked to me about my studies, a subject on which I needed no coaching from Claude. He had a way of questioning me that made the answers easy, and Claude did not interpose. I was proud of this rapid success. But his mother did not accept me. At our first meeting I understood her. This was her son. No girl in the world would ever be good enough for him.

"Is this the siren who has bewitched my Claude?" she said to me by way of greeting. The look her husband threw her was not a tender one. She didn't notice it, but kept up this mincing manner all through luncheon. On top of this, the meal itself was a bad one—since Madame Guichard was no cook. Claude had already told me, "My mother looks down on cooking and housework. She sees herself as an intellectual. She goes to literary tea-parties, meetings of the Alliance Française and that kind of crap." She treated us to a discourse on the extraordinary good fortune of modern youth in being able to "draw strength from the sources of European culture, where all is beauty, etc." I listened politely to this interminable nonsense. After many farewells I was able to leave. Claude went with me.

"It's in the bag," he said. "Thanks to you. I'm very grateful."

He kissed me, for once, with genuine warmth.

112

At the end of May the great college dispersion took place. In a last attempt to prolong my studies I had applied for a scholarship. The other students in the faculty warned me. "To win a scholarship you must have pull. Get a letter from your member or someone in the government." I didn't even know I had a member. I knew no one in the government or anywhere else. The Guillaumes suggested I contact some friends of theirs. I refused.

"Either I deserve a scholarship, or I don't."

"Still little Miss Inflexible? I'm afraid you're due for a blow."

And what a blow it was! I was dumbfounded to learn the names of the winners. Even Claude was one of them. I hid my dismay. They all winged their joyous way to Europe, coupling up like birds. I was left behind, witless, jobless, grasping my diploma.

113

At that time an Arts degree was of no earthly use. I soon realized this. To satisfy the various school commissions one had to have a teacher's certificate. I simply could not pay for the two additional years of study required to obtain one. A humble application to the Sisters might have given me a few hours a week teaching school. They always held it their duty to "help out former students." I could not descend to this. So I looked elsewhere. To begin with, I tried to exercise some choice. I went the rounds. The newspapers, the magazines, the weeklies. They laughed in my face.

"You've had some experience?"

Where on earth could I have got any? Faced with my bewilderment, they simply showed me the door, more or less politely, and rather less than more. I was discovering with dismay another dimension of the social contract. Until now I'd thought one had only to work hard at school in order to graduate to some kind of apprenticeship —while keeping one's nose to the grindstone, behaving oneself and doing one's best. Now I found that work itself was a privilege, a chance to be jumped at, something one had to beg for. The rest of my class were all settled in their jobs; I still had no idea where to turn.

"It's much harder for girls. In this country journalism

is a job for men," a journalist confided. Then I understood why I was always told there was no position open on the women's pages of the newspapers. Any test for the kind of work I was looking for was flatly refused. After a few more categorical refusals, I gave up asking.

I no longer dared apply anywhere. I was disgusted by this discrimination about which no one had told me. I was used to not being "in demand" in the amatory field, but I thought I would at least be allowed to do the kind of work I liked—only to find this too was preserved ground. I used to sob with discouragement in the hideous room I had rented with some damnable people who kept their radio going full blast from morning till night. This row at least prevented them from hearing the sounds of my grief. I made the most of it by weeping at my ease.

114

I studied the classified advertisements. I applied for every position offered, but I always lacked some qualification or other. Of course I should have appealed to the few friends and connections my parents had made. I couldn't bring myself to do this.

Danielle was married. A splendid wedding, with a crush of guests. Her parents were worried about me. They telephoned to find out what I was doing.

"I've found nothing." My voice trembled.

Thanks to them I managed to find a "place."

"It's only temporary, dear little Hélène. After that, you'll find something in your own line."

I thanked them effusively. This "temporary" job kept me going for five years.

So now I too had my "hole." I don't know when this frightful word made its way into the vocabulary. I'm inclined to think it was during that period when the whole ambition of a betrayed generation simply amounted to securing a place in "the sunshine of work." Thanks to my parents, I had escaped the bomb-shelters. I now found myself lodged for years in this other shelter from life itself.

116

I was a *receptionist*. That was my official title. In a private radio station where songs were interspersed with the listeners' write-ins on a variety of subjects: love, cookery, the soul. My multifarious duties could have inspired a sparkling couplet in some play by Beaumarchais. I took on every job the others refused, as well as being an all-day telephone switchboard. Delighted at being no longer "out of work," I would do anything at all. I skipped lunch and stayed on till long after closing, catching up on the day's arrears of work. It became a habit; everything passed through my hands. I was "indispensable," a "treasure." Since I could type and had "a way with words"—as my boss frankly admitted—I was allowed to rewrite the listeners' mail.

"Go ahead, fix it up . . ."

Glad to be so appreciated, I got through everything.

"They're exploiting you," Danielle protested. "That's not your job. Insist on giving a broadcast yourself. Then they'll have to pay you what you're worth."

The very idea of going before a microphone froze me

with terror. I paid her no attention. From time to time I was given a raise in pay, and accepted it with gratitude.

117

Time went by. Whether fast or slowly, I had no idea. Does the bear remember his winter sleep? In the detective stories I read at night, the suspects could always account for every moment of their day. I'm unable to give the smallest detail of those five years: nothing will emerge. I managed to live from one day to the next, rising early and working tirelessly all day long. But then there were the evenings—the horrible evenings I had to kill. I put off the moment when I would find myself alone within my four walls. For I had my own walls now. I had taken a small bachelor apartment with a kitchenette and a dilapidated bathroom. I hoped to feel at home at last. By degrees I "furnished" it. With pine-wood pieces which I enamelled in bright colours. "How amusing!" exclaimed the few visitors to this "pad." It was hideous, and I knew it. Not only due to the lack of money: several of my friends who were no better off had managed to make their surroundings pleasant at no greater cost. The place was dark and badly laid out. I couldn't manage to give it any character. Material things have always *resisted* me. I didn't know how to choose them or impress my personality on them. I was overcome by the same apathy when faced with furniture, objects, even food. Everything seemed to call for too much effort. On waking I always suffered from nausea. I threw myself into my work, where I was of some use. I answered the telephone while everyone around me was coming and going, and gave speedy and accurate information. I was glad just to be busy, I welcomed the work. Nobly, I volunteered for all the unpleasant jobs. I kept lengthening my hours at the office. I must have made the others feel guilty, for they began pushing me out every night. I was literally forced to leave. With the shops all closed, I was reduced to my restaurant. I always went to the same place, a huge pizza and spaghetti factory, ugly and anonymous. I had no need to give my order: they knew me. I swallowed my spaghetti and watched the others consuming theirs. My Operation Food was "finalized" in fifteen minutes. Furtively, I would then slip into the nearest cinema. At that time the show comprised two features and the news reel; sometimes, for good measure, a few short features as well. I watched, passively. When a good film was being shown I carefully avoided it. I wanted to remain in my unreal condition of brutishness. Lulled by the remembered whistling of arrows and the sound of six-shooters, I would go to bed. At last I fell asleep.

118

Then there were the week-ends. And the holidays. Getting through them was harder than the week itself. To punish myself, I had given up reading. I had deprived myself of this joy, this nourishment. During these barren years I fed on nothing but rubbish. I shunned even the sight of books. A little dead-alive girl of twenty-two.

119

A dead young girl, a living old one. Throughout the years of full-blown youth I was nothing but a whining old woman, frightened of everything, exhausted by everything in advance. Samples of earth can be radiographed, and their history determined. I would like to plumb the subterranean character of this period of my life. Some strange undiscovered illness might explain this wretched lethargy of mine, this personal ice age when everything was fossilized, turned to stone.

These days people try to flatter me by saying I look younger than my age. This only hurts me; for in my own lilac-time I plucked no blossoms—and I shall never reach the age of quiet reason. This false appearance of youth only serves to recall my wasted years.

120

A woman untimely old, prolonging her false youth: this is my double aspect. I'll soon pass from superannuated girl to simple corpse. Without any transition, any enjoyment of mature happiness.

121

For ten years I lived in your shadow. Ten whole years. And with one backhand stroke you got rid of me—and of all those summers, those bright June mornings, those long winter nights. Ten years. My lease was cancelled without notice or consultation. "Go away. You're a nuisance." Nietzsche declares that "the suffering we inflict is more real than the suffering we endure." You must be wallowing in reality. While I feel I am struggling in an unreal nightmare. I can hardly believe it.

If I'd only been a "real woman." But long ago I put myself beyond the pale of my sex. Women are persons who get married, whose opinions are respected. Men bleed themselves white to leave such women their life insurance. As for me, you dismissed me like a servant, without even a month's notice. I had only to apply that much sooner for "social security." Fancy anyone like you breaking the rules laid down by "nice people!"

123

In that summer of our love—it was a flash of summer lightning, a swift roll of thunder—I was ready to do anything. I would have plunged into hell itself to be with you. Gladly. You on the other hand carefully weighed your words and your gifts. As if love were not a folly that's always out of season. To follow you, I would have gone down to hell. Just to follow you! I followed the road that inevitably leads there, but alone.

124

When I was twenty-five I chose two worthy mentors. Thérèse and Marguerite. Two sisters in their forties, not quite twins, who came every evening to my restaurant—"to save both time and money," as they explained after I had come to know them. They were a strange pair, immense, laconic, dressed in quasi-military fashion. At first I thought they belonged to the Salvation Army. They had noticed me on account of my frugality, "remarkable in a girl so young." They wondered why I always ordered the same thing; they discussed this. Marguerite was convinced I was fulfilling some vow in a spirit of religious mortification. Since they were curious, and since "curiosity, as a path to knowledge, was not to be scorned," they asked me about it. I was stupefied, not knowing what to say. Thérèse interposed kindly, "There are other dishes just as reasonably priced. This way, you will ruin your digestion."

They themselves had been frightfully poor. By sheer force of character they had "gotten out of their milieu." Marguerite was a medical secretary. Thérèse a librarian. Finding I had been "right through college," they decided to take me up.

"You mustn't let your learning go to waste."

I didn't tell them I had learned nothing. For them, the university stood for an unattainable ideal. I would have disappointed them if I had admitted that one was no more enlightened on leaving than on entering it.

One day they asked me to their place for Sunday luncheon. I accepted. They had gone to infinite pains in preparing the meal: it was made up of "health foods" containing all the vitamins they thought I was not getting—grated carrots, wheat germ, calf's liver. I was touched by their kindness. After luncheon they took me to the Botanical Gardens. Every week they went on such instructive outings. Their knowledge of Montreal and its outskirts was extraordinary. I didn't doubt Danielle would have looked on them as *Holy Terrors*, so I kept this friendship to myself. They adopted me as their "spiritual daughter." Marguerite and Thérèse were the first happy spinsters I had ever known. They would have liked to have children if it could be done without the offices of a man. They were convinced that parthenogenesis would soon do away with "all that kind of thing."

Their father, a household tyrant, had confirmed them

in their horror of men and marriage. Ardent feminists, they were politically oriented and active in all good causes. I was ashamed of my apathy of the past few years. They dragged me to socialist meetings and to marches on foreign embassies. I was just beginning to take an interest in world problems, to emerge from my egoistic shell, when Claude returned suddenly from Paris. His father had died.

125

He had written me fairly regularly during the past five years. Nice, funny little letters. At his request I had sent New Year's greetings to his parents, thus keeping up the fiction of our "engagement." Of course I went to the funeral.

Now that she was a widow, Claude's mother was determined to hold on to him. He sensed the danger. His mother had always suffered from a hundred imaginary ailments; by now she was a confirmed hypochondriac. Whenever he left her alone for the evening he would return to find her in tears: she had had another "heart attack." He never clearly explained the provisions of his father's will to me, but I gathered that he must make a choice: get married or live with Madame Mère. He therefore made me the following "proposal": a grand formal wedding in Montreal; then a long trip to Europe on the pretext of "finishing" his thesis. I could continue my studies also, at the Sorbonne. This last was what decided me: to read, write and work freely, without financial cares. Claude spoke in glowing terms of the life we would lead: the pretty apartment in Paris, the trips to Italy and Greece in the summer.

"You'll be quite independent. We'll arrange everything like good friends. Each of us on our own, in absolute freedom." By our marriage contract he would settle so much on me, "to do just as you want with." I had never known him to be so kind, so studious to soften the slights his mother kept slyly putting on me. To "keep her busy," he suggested she go with me to choose my trousseau —where with consummate verbal skill she contrived to make nasty remarks in a sugary tone that only emphasized their venom.

I was quite miserable, while everyone loaded me with congratulations and good wishes. I felt that this "happy ending" was a great surprise to them. I had been classed with those girls who are left on the shelf, the hopeless old maids. And here I had succeeded in making "a good match." All of a sudden Claude, the Son and Heir, had made everyone forget the failed Eternal Student of old.

Thanks to his years in Europe he had acquired a few more coats of varnish, a studied accent and better clothes. It was allowed that he had acquired "good form." Now that he had plenty of money no one cared how he had come by it.

The date of our wedding was approaching. I grew terrified, and had no one to confide in. At the office I was given a big party. With nothing to do, I now had all day to think. The clearance of my apartment was soon effected. Even Marguerite and Thérèse were delighted. They made me promise to pursue my studies seriously. A husband who wanted his wife to study was as one set apart and above the others: he escaped their proscription of men in general. Moreover, Claude had put himself out to please them, and they found him "remarkable."

Claude took great pains to convince everyone of the "reality" of this marriage. As for me, I was in a cold sweat: it seemed the imposture was all too patent. Every moment I expected to wake up, to hear some swelling burst of laughter announce the end of the comedy. These grownup people, cool, well-informed, sophisticated, actually took this masquerade at its face value. I was astonished to discover their want of malice. As long as one pretended to play their game they asked no further questions. No one examined my motives for marrying Claude: they were both obvious and correct. Marriage was a matter of security and material comfort, and a hedge against loneliness.

So I prepared to barter my "little Russian soul" for a good middle-class conscience, with absolute impunity. There were moments when I found it laughable to be playing the role of heroine in one of the sentimental novels of my girlhood, the ones abounding in "white" marriages. Alas, I had no one with whom to laugh.

126

No more ambiguity or misunderstanding now between Claude and me, only sincere friendship. The past, with all its foolish abortive caresses, was dead. I had stifled that strange desire for suffering to which my self-loathing had carried me.

127

I was discovering with astonishment that the "foolishness" of the good Sisters was not so foolish as it had seemed. I enjoyed a certain peace only in my periods of "latency," as the psychiatrists would say, or of "purity" as the sisters would have called them. But important things are never properly explained to us at the right time. Popular songs and idiotic phrases about the "thraldom of the flesh" speak more clearly to whomever cares to listen. With Michel and Claude my suffering was unimportant. But I gave myself wholly to you. Body and soul. And here I am now, lost and lacking either.

Lost, by my own choice. I could always have drawn back, drawn away. When we met I was free and happy. My fate hung in the balance: I could choose. And then that dream, so vivid: *A knock at my door; I went and opened it to you; I invited you in. You lay down beside me; I took you in my arms. Then I saw it was death I was clasping so tenderly to my heart.* And truly it is death you have brought me: the initial death-struggles, spasms of pain, tortures of anguish. Now the very centres of life are affected. I knew it all along. Why rebel?

128

As I squarely faced the church wedding on which Claude insisted—"my family wouldn't think of us not going before Monsieur le Curé"—my scruples recurred. I was not a practising Christian, but I had a dread of sacrilege. I was not misled by the gravity of the ceremony. "A pure formality," Claude assured me. Now that he was "officially" engaged, he stuck at nothing. "You're not going to put on airs, are you?"

He took after his mother, and could be just as cruel. Europe had transformed him inwardly as well as outwardly: before he left Canada he was not so cynically bent on brushing any obstacle from his path. I was to find this out to my cost. Like a fool, I let myself be led to an altar where I was to sacrifice not only my life but my integrity.

I dreaded the pre-marital act of confession. Claude had also given it some thought. He made an appointment for me.

"Father Berthiaume is an old friend of mine. He will receive you as a matter of form. I told him you were temperamental."

He went along with me. Leaving me with the warning, "No silly tricks, now. Don't say anything. Let him do the talking."

When I saw the priest I began to weep. The tears blinded me; desperately I sought my handkerchief. Father Berthiaume was very old. Very good too, no doubt. He was content to give me his absolution and wish me a happy wedded life.

"Well?" Claude asked.

"It's over."

I was almost sorry the priest hadn't asked me for a simple yes or no. I'm sure I could not have lied convincingly: at his first question I would have crumbled. And I thought of the irony of my childhood confessions when, having to admit nothing but peccadilloes, I was bombarded with uncouth and indiscreet questions. Now, when I was about to bind myself "till death us do part," it wasn't thought advisable to impress me with the gravity of my act.

No, I am still lying. I did know what I was doing. I alone am to blame. Interrogated, catechized, I would have lied with calm effrontery. Well, I was spared the commission of actual perjury.

Claude was still in mourning for his father, so the marriage was to be performed "quietly," and I escaped the ordeal of the bridal gown. Madame Guichard was torn between the grief of "losing her Claude" and the pleasure of revelling in an orgy of worldliness. She almost drove the milliner and the dressmaker mad. Her list of wedding guests grew daily. Claude gave her a free hand. He was ready to grant her anything to keep her quiet.

I myself had invited the Guillaumes and Danielle and her husband. Dr. Guillaume was to give me away. I would not have dared to ask him, but he had kindly offered—as the head of my "adoptive family." On Claude's side, the kinsmen were multiplying: from Chicoutimi, Trois-Rivières, Quebec. I envied him all these relatives, these "connections" he pretended to despise but for whom this edifying religious ceremony was after all being performed.

Once again I was making the excruciating discovery of my aloneness. I would have liked to feel surrounded, supported, upheld by my roots and rights. My own parents had given each other that kind of unshakeable loving assurance which makes up for all other wants and insufficiencies. Once again I found myself in the vacuum they had deliberately created around us. Already I foresaw my marriage would make me more vulnerable than ever.

Madame Guillaume was the soul of kindness. She bought me dozens of pretty things for my trousseau and helped me choose my going away costume. She seemed to want me to confide in her. Several times I was tempted to disclose my secret. But she was so far from suspecting the truth, and would have been so deeply shocked by it, that I refrained.

On the eve of my wedding I sobbed all night long, only

breaking off from time to time to put cold compresses on my face to avoid being disfigured the following day. Thanks to Madame Guillaume, who made me up skilfully without seeming to notice my ravaged face, I was presentable on the great day.

131

That awful day. As girls, we dream for years of this famous day. I was like a sleepwalker, moving from right to left, worked like a marionette, letting myself be kissed, embraced, looked at, questioned. Nothing else is clear. Yet I could recall every detail of this "longest day," if I were to try.

All through the ceremony at the church my whole problem was attempting to breathe. To breathe calmly, as I had been taught to do in moments of panic when one is frightened of drowning. I bent all my efforts towards controlling my breathing; above all not to weep, not to add this grotesque detail to the circus. Madame Guichard gave the assemblage their full ration of tears, with great artistry. Claude himself was quite put in the shade. The two of them made a fantastic couple: Oedipus and Jocasta in all their glory, before the truth comes out. The relatives from out of town had their money's worth: for them, it was well worth the trip to Montreal. As for me, I took refuge among the Guillaumes. Danielle had resumed all her affection for me, and all her earlier kindness. They were the only witnesses of my past life, of those ten wasted years whose bitterness they had tried to sweeten. When it was time for me to leave they all kissed me, repeating, "You're starting a new life."

132

It was to start very badly. The first stage was New York, our port of embarkation. I had paid little attention to Claude when he was outlining his plans. But now this port seemed to augur ill. But I could say nothing. I went along silently.

133

After the infernal hubbub of our departure, the quietness of the train. I was glad to take refuge in our reserved compartment. Claude left me there and announced, without suggesting that I go with him, that he was going to have a drink in the bar: "I need one."

I had been hoping for some compliment on my performance, but he seemed unwilling to say anything. Since it had been a trying day for him too—his mother had not spared the farewell sobs—I made the best of it.

134

I ended by falling asleep. When I awoke Claude had still not come back, and I went to look for him. I saw him, or rather heard him, from some distance. He was still in the club car, glass in hand. The waiter, obviously out of all patience, was facing me, while Claude had his back to me. He was speaking English, very loudly, in a shrill piercing voice I had never heard before, and waving his arms. I left without him seeing me. We reached New York before he returned to the compartment.

135

We were not due to sail till evening. Claude had taken a hotel room, to "freshen us up a little." Once there, he fell on one of the twin beds and fell asleep fully clothed. I watched him for a few moments. Fully dressed and even wearing his shoes, his hands tightly clasped and his face buried in the pillow, he seemed as much on the defensive as some knight of the Middle Ages in his armour. I decided to let him sleep. I didn't dare go down alone to order breakfast: I, the young bride of yesterday! I seated myself by the window. As I had done long ago in the same city. Gazing at the clouds sailing by in this end-of-August sky. From time to time my body trembled. In his sleep, Claude was grinding his teeth.

136

He woke around noon in a bad temper. "I've a mouth like the bottom of a birdcage." He looked at me accusingly. "I'll bet you're hungry." I *was* hungry. He took a shower and changed his clothes. Then he picked up the telephone: "Sorry, I have to make a call." Wishing to be discreet, I locked myself in the bathroom. But his conversation reached me. He was being all charm and graciousness. But not for me: "I'll drop you off at the cafeteria. I couldn't eat a thing. I'm off to have a drink with a couple of friends. I'll be back around four."

137

He came back at six. We had to make a dash for the boat. He made no excuses. All at once, feeling intolerably confined in his hateful presence, I was tempted to flee. Now that I had become his legal property he thought he could do anything he liked with me. I was boiling with rage, and also feeling the terror of an animal caught in a trap. Claude must have sensed my fury. By the time we reached our cabin he had regained a little politeness.

138

The boat weighed anchor, and Claude went to the bar. I remained on deck, standing among the crowd of passengers waving their handkerchiefs. There was no one to bid me goodbye. And no one on board to bid me welcome. It was almost twenty years since my mother had bravely declared, "We're going to be very happy in America," and refused to look back at the receding coast of France. I was retracing the same course in reverse. I cast a quick look at Manhattan dwindling behind, and forced myself to look at the open sea.

139

The sea was rough. I passed my time in being seasick, confined to our cabin. In the bar, Claude kept drinking with such persistence that he made himself sick as well. We had little to say to each other. Now and then he proposed we take a turn on deck, and I followed him. He would buttonhole the passengers with whom he had already scraped acquaintance and introduce me to them: "This is Hélène, my wife." As if I were a prize of war.

When I ventured on deck alone I would soon come across him strutting along and keeping his weather eye open. Officers, sailors and stewards held a special fascination for him. I was finding out that Claude, as well as being homosexual, had an immoderate craving for drink and uniforms. I paid no attention: I did not wish to interfere. But as soon as I began chatting with anyone he never failed to break in on the conversation; he would then carry me off on some pretext or other, only to drop me abruptly a few moments later. This curious display of jealousy did not seem to fit in with the terms of our agreement, that pact of perfect reciprocal freedom to which I had subscribed in all good faith. I was beginning to doubt his word.

At last we reached Le Havre, and then Paris. Claude then announced he had let his apartment to friends, and that we would take a room in a hotel. He chose a pretentious and expensive hotel on the Right Bank, full of damasked armchairs and gilded chandeliers. Our room was dark and smothered in deep red velvet curtains which gave it a funereal air. An enormous bed was enthroned in the middle. The boy had barely left before I told Claude to demand another room. He seemed astonished. "Why? Don't you like the way it's furnished?" I persisted: "Ask for a room with two beds." "Ah, we're in France, my dear. There's no such thing."

142

All that day I tried not to think of the coming night. Claude quite kindly took me around a Paris which I barely recognized. Deep in my thoughts, I saw nothing.

"You look quite *ruined*," he said with a laugh.

It was foolish of me to be upset. Having agreed to perjure myself, I had no longer any excuse to play the prude. I had apparently sold myself, body and soul.

143

Claude took me to a big restaurant for dinner, where he ordered our meal with care. He had called for champagne, and at dessert he raised his glass: "To the bride." I had only time to make a headlong dash, wave the lavabos woman aside, and throw up. I insisted on going back to the hotel on foot, declaring that I needed fresh air.

144

Once we were in our room Claude produced a bottle of whisky from his suitcase. "Take all the time you want. I'll have a drink while I'm waiting. Don't forget, this is the night we celebrate our wedding."

I could have fled, or argued, or threatened to expose him. I did not. I undressed in the bathroom, taking as long as I dared. When I came back Claude was in bed. The level in the bottle was considerably reduced. I got in beside him and he turned out the light.

In the darkness, without a single kiss or caress, he passed to the attack. I was torn between the desire to accede, so as to get this "rape" over with as quickly as possible, and such a sense of rebellion that I kept fighting artfully to keep him from reaching his goal. Suddenly he turned on the light. He poured himself another drink and then looked me straight in the face. "I've known you to be more sociable." I made no reply. As he came against me once more his whisky-laden breath turned my stomach. To gain a little time I asked him, "Why? Why this?" He laughed. "To make the marriage indissoluble, of course! After tonight you'll never be able to get an annulment. Our marriage will be consummated. Before God and man."

I had bound myself to a base, contemptible rogue. Even the sight of him was so unbearable that I turned out the light myself. He resumed his task, and kept on ineptly. I made no further resistance. Now and then an oath escaped him. Once his aim was achieved he fell asleep immediately. I wept soundlessly in the darkness. This flood of tears was my only relief, wiping out the insult done to my body, washing away the blood he had shed.

We awoke. I too had at last fallen asleep. I woke up aching in every limb. Claude, in fine fettle and playing the innocent, suggested all kinds of things for us to do. I said I was ill. He offered to remain "at my bedside"; I opposed this strongly. At last he left, declaring, "I'll be back around five o'clock. In the meantime have a good rest."

An hour later the chambermaid knocked at the door

and came in bearing a huge basket of flowers. I pretended to be floating in the seventh heaven of delight.

147

This time Claude came back punctually. We were to have a drink together and then dine with some friends of his. I was delighted to escape being alone with him. He was full of little attentions to me. Before the two other couples, who appeared to be "straight," he played to perfection the part of the kind, considerate husband. He allowed me to "sleep" in peace all that night.

148

Lying there in the darkness, beside this man I had begun to hate, I could not sleep. Huddled in my own corner of the bed, I kept as far from him as I could. "I hate him, I hate him . . ." I kept reciting this litany while my tears continued to fall, copiously and without ceasing.

149

Claude hated me in return. His feigned kindness no longer imposed on me. Without saying a word to him I went to the Sorbonne and filled out the innumerable entry forms. More than ever I was determined to seek my freedom through study.

150

When I came back he made a scene.

"Where have you been?"

He must have been drinking all day. That night, once again and in a kind of fury, he "made love" to me. Nothing was less like love than this ignoble contest between us. He fell upon me as if he had some vengeance to wreak, some old debt to pay; as if, in me, all women were being scored off.

"I hate this man. I hate him. I despise him." And yet I was afraid lest I should come to destest, in him, all men. To reassure myself I kept telling myself he was not really a man at all. "Only a poor imitation."

151

The days that followed were a kind of inferno. He never left me for a moment. I walked, ate and slept at his-side—at once dejected and maddened with rage. On the quays, among a heap of soiled secondhand books I found a copy of *Thérèse Desqueyroux*.[4] I re-read it with exquisite enjoyment. Hounded like Thérèse, I fled into dreams of murder. When Claude held me beneath him I escaped him in fancy, devising the tortures I in turn would inflict on him. One night, utterly exhausted, I ventured to ask, "What are you trying to prove? Your virility?" I was laughing, with no notion of his reply. "Don't worry, my dear, as soon as you're pregnant we'll give up these vile gymnastics."

It was like a thunder-stroke. At last I understood. Too
late, perhaps. Claude appeared astonished: "Didn't you
know?" I didn't want him to know he had gulled me once
again. But he wasn't taken in. "You're quite wrong about
men like me," he went on. "We often make excellent
fathers of large families. But it's up to you, my dear. A son
and heir will be enough for me."

I was annihilated. Through this child Claude would
have a hold on me forever. A child of his. My child. This
perverse, ridiculous marriage would simply generate
another little scrap of life. I felt an infinite pity for this
being to be brought forth, this victim of such absurd and
ignoble parents. After her daughter's birth Thérèse had
tried to kill her husband. I was beginning to understand
how she had passed from fantasy to action. My own
homicidal rage against Claude had burnt itself out: for me,
he was morally dead. All that mattered now was my own
self and the life I might be carrying within me. I did not
know which to choose: suicide or abortion. To be on the
safe side, and seeing that in any case I would need money,
I cabled my bank in Montreal to transfer funds to Paris.
Within a week I would know for certain. Claude must
have made the same calculation. From now on he left me
in peace.

153

I did not dare pray. But every hour I passionately be-
sought a kindly tutelary power to spare me this martyr-
dom of maternity. The week went by. Claude said
nothing: he was exulting. I pretended indifference. One
day when he was forgathering with his *friends* I paid a

swift visit to a doctor I had chosen at random. I described my insomnia to him so convincingly that he gave me a prescription for a whole tube of sleeping pills. With these in my possession I felt easier: I could make a painless exit whenever I chose. Alone and without a single acquaintance in Paris, I would never be able to find an abortionist. Moreover, I found it only fitting to die along with "my child." For my parents I myself had been an unfortunate mistake. I would not inflict the same ordeal on another. With me the chain of error would be broken.

154

From you, my dear, I desired a child. Passionately. A little boy with sparkling eyes, plump ankles, silken wispy hair. A lovely boy in the likeness of his father. You laughed at this "preposterous" desire. And during the ten years of our liaison you gave your lawful wedded wife three other lawful heirs. I have been punished for my sins.

155

A week later. Ten days. . . . I had allowed myself a month. Panic seized me: such a deadline was absurd! I no longer hoped for a "miracle." My only thought was how to carry out my plan of suicide. I was terrified of the least thing going wrong. Claude was watching me like a hawk: he was obviously suspicious. On some pretext or other he had taken possession of my passport. To begin with I had thought of hiding in some quiet little hotel where I could "go to sleep" until it was too late to be found. But without any identification I would be unable to take a room. So I remained where I was, hypnotized by my own helplessness, weighing my chances night and day, devising impossible stratagems. Sure of his new power over me, Claude was gloating.

156

You have abandoned me. And here I am. Liberated. With nothing between me and death. Only a mindless appetite for living can save me. You have succeeded in reducing me to despair; you have even destroyed the traces of whatever sweetness we shared in the past. I have no future. The homely suffering of "the great unloved," you don't know what it is. But I know all too well that pungent sickness. In the theatre, whenever I hear the eternal female plaint, I weep. Ah, these women have a voice to publish their pain! A man puts the words into their mouth. Listening to Claudel's *L'Echange* I suffer with Marthe, I envy Lechy her savage cries. I had no words to utter in my own defense. You talked, you reasoned. But suffering had taken my breath away. You praised my "courage," my "docility." As in the gas chambers, there was no protest. I hate you for reaching the same refinement of cruelty and cowardice. You didn't even barter me for anything rarer and more precious. You simply dropped me like something worn out—worse, like those broken toys that rich people give to poor children who'll be "so glad to have them." You even had the effrontery to suggest I might have a happy future with another man—a man who could make me happy and be happy in the enjoyment of your leavings.

157

I can remember this betrayal now, for the final curtain is about to fall. I shan't spoil my dénouement! I've botched everything until now. Every word I've set down here only confirms my nonentity, my appetite for disaster. I have planned all the details of my last act, and I keep polishing them with a kind of loving, maniacal care.

158

I didn't fall asleep till dawn. Then I fell into a profound slumber, catching up with Claude. I dreamed I was swimming in a seagreen pool where strange pink and orange fish threaded their way among the reeds. I floated there, careless, free, happy, with dragonflies hovering around me. Slowly I sank into the depths from which a wonderful light was rising. I reached the bottom. The sand was warm. I lay among sea-shells. I heard strange music, and yet I knew I was dead, drowned and re-deemed.

159

When I awoke my thighs were bathed in warm blood as red as rubies. The bed was spotted with darker stains. I roused Claude. He noted the damage and only muttered, "Now we'll have to start all over again."

160

For me it was a new lease on life. I felt such a surge of

thankfulness that I no longer thought of exulting over Claude. I let him sleep on. I spent the rest of the night mapping out the stages of my journey to freedom.

In the morning I told him my plans.

"I'm leaving you. Give me back my passport. If you refuse I'll go to the Embassy."

He realized I was escaping him for good.

"What do you mean to do? Get even with me? Tell everything? Blackmail?"

I swore to hold my "damages" to a minimum. It was then arranged that we would part "by mutual agreement" on the grounds of incompatibility. I would not apply for a divorce, but for a legal separation later on. Since I meant to study for my doctorate in Paris there would be no need to publicize the matter in Montreal.

"You want money?" he asked.

"I'll manage with what you've given me already. I can make it last while I'm in France. When I'm back in Canada and earning money I'll pay you back."

He pretended not to believe me. But I kept my word. This was a debt I discharged to the last cent.

161

For three years I lived peacefully. Was this happiness? I had never been so close to it. I was grateful for this intermission. Everything went smoothly. After the waking nightmare of my marriage—that successor of my long sleep of continence—I was glad merely to exist. Like a convalescent rediscovering the bliss of the simplest bodily movements. My attic room was icy cold and without running water, but I slept soundly in it; I stood in line at the university restaurants, but I ate with appetite. Once again I was reading voraciously. I was immersed in the actual, in the sights and sounds of the streets no less than in my work. My thesis was coming along steadily. Once again I felt the stimulus of work, the thirst for knowledge, the desire for self-expression. At this time I wrote poems and review articles. I ventured to show them around, and they were published. My mind was at rest, my body at ease. I had never had less money, but I wore cheap clothes in comfort. I no longer expected anything from the world around me. Neither love nor friendship. I was contented. Living for the moment.

162

Why quarrel with fate? Our meeting was in the cards. And yet since I was once happy in utter solitude I should be able to repeat the experience now. The joys of work, reading and travel are still open to me. Ah, but I've no longer the strength to grasp them. Only a telephone that no longer rings, and certain words traced in your hand-writing, could revive my heartbeat. Nothing else can touch or reach me. Age also is playing its terrible part. It's not only these wrinkles, this vanished bloom of health. You are a doctor, you know that after a certain age the least fracture is hard to set, unlikely to knit. I have now reached that threshhold of fragility. In bits and pieces. Drawn and quartered by suffering. I refuse to heal. My flesh rebels at the bare idea of forming new scars.

163

Oh you made a fine mess of things. I had a hand in it too. I rebel against the idea of putting these words on paper, the innocent words that will bring our guilty encounter back to life. Yet I've only been scribbling all these pages with that end in view. The stage is empty. I could ring down the curtain, and announce that the "heavy" disclaims his competence to act, says the part is too unrewarding. But I won't. I must bring you on, give the three knocks. In the theatre, this is the moment I like best. The stage is empty; the set is arranged; everything is in place; the tragedy can begin. We already know it will end in blood and tears at the close of the fifth act, within the prescribed twenty-four hours.

A single action in a single day and place . . .[5]

That was how it was played out between us. But you made me wait ten years for the dénouement.

164

Right from the start you acted in bad faith. There's a fine passage of Benjamin Constant's where Adolphe exclaims, "Woe betide him who, in the first moments of love's fulfilment, does not believe his love is eternal." You never believed yours would be. You embarked on an "adventure," knowing you could end it whenever you liked. Yet in your eagerness to make this fleshly conquest you swore you were in love. I was so dazzled, so carried away, that I believed you. Well, there are imitation lovers, as there are imitation gamblers. The latter are all too obvious. I watch them here as they get ready for the casino. Prudently, they take their "stake" with them: twenty dollars, perhaps fifty. And prudently they leave the rest—all the money needed for food and lodging—behind in the hotel safe. Then they go and "gamble." And they come back proudly announcing, "I have lost everything!" Fancying they have known the gambler's passion. You were as passionate as these prudent tourists. As for me, I staked everything on this one throw, without hesitation or regret.

165

My time is running out. The holidays are almost over and I can't bring myself to launch into the last chapter. Ten years. A decade, and a debacle. From the woman of thirty to the woman of forty. The passage from summer to fall. The days grow shorter; the dark extends its kindly reign. If only I could recall how it was between us at first! Then I'm sure I would be saved. But I have destroyed even its memory. I have torn up everything, burnt everything: not one letter or photograph is left. A clean sweep. So my death will do you no harm. Nothing and no one will connect this "accidental" death in Venice with your fine Canadian career. Sleep soundly, my dear. Though I myself am now sleepless, I husband my resources: I keep my little store of pills intact. I'll have just the right dose, just enough to dress this suicide as an accident, and no more. No scandal attached to it: my suffering has been well hidden. No one has noticed anything at the hotel here. I'm a model guest: early to bed and early to rise, eating whatever is put in front of me, never raising my voice, giving the appearance of perfect serenity. If they have given me any nickname here it must be *the placid one*: the commonplace, the seemly one. I will spare them, too, the slightest trouble. In my room my bags will be packed, my bill paid the day before my "departure," everything seen to. I'll even have given out my tips—brightly, pleasantly, assuring everyone how much I've enjoyed my stay. My seat on the plane will be reserved. I shan't overlook anything.

166

My strength is giving out. My flesh can no longer bear the strain of this assumed calm. It is taking more and more effort to keep my voice down, my hands steady. For I am still waiting. I've devised the excuse of writing this "novel" to pass the time. While I'm waiting for some word from you.

167

There is no use waiting. I know I can expect no miracle, no commutation of my sentence. I was asking for so little. But what excuse could you have had? I have imagined them all, created them to order. There is no comfortable lie I haven't told myself. At the very beginning you told me the truth: "I am incapable of love." I didn't believe you. How could such a being keep on living? I am reading Lowry's *Under the Volcano,* or at least trying to. And I found this sentence, *"Non se puede vivir sin amar."* How do you manage to do it? I am killing myself, because without love I am no longer alive.

168

When the spirit is dead, the flesh is still rebellious. For the past two days I have had fever: sharp attacks that leave me trembling and in a sweat. Confined to my room, I can no longer see the postman arrive or the manager filling the pigeonholes with letters for other people. For me, there is no mail. But why should you write?

In the hotel they are worried: they propose sending

for a doctor. I pretend to feel better. The toilet receives
the food they bring me on trays.

169

Pierre, listen. Do something. You have no right to abandon a human being to despair. You have taken the Hip-
pocratic oath. There are laws to protect people in distress.
"Failure to assist anyone in danger." You will be judged
and sentenced. You have left me without hope. I am dry
as ashes: nothing can draw one tear from me, one cry of
complaint. I am already dead. Even if you came to me
now, offering all the sweets of the earth, I would not have
the strength to take them. Like the traveller long lost in
the desert, I know that all hope of water is a mirage.

170

Pierre: the fine prophetic name your mother gave you.
Hard as stone. Stubborn, turned in upon yourself, concerned only with your own precious person. I have a
vision of the final scene: I will be embarking for death, and
you will be quietly busy playing golf or bridge. What do I
know of the dozens of stupid games that you find it important to excel at and "win"? All the while pluming yourself
on your seriousness, your prudence, your good sense.
For you really believe you are *virtuous*. Haven't you led a
"good" life ever since you broke off that "sordid affair"?
You're right: it was sordid. Not for a moment did you
suspect the truth, did you feel any guilt. Well, live on in
your misty moral universe! For ten years I tried to make
you accept my vision of the world. You didn't know what

to make of it. And so I leave you to your clear and shining conscience.

171

I couldn't have really loved you. Otherwise I would find it easier to excuse your weaknesses, I could forgive you, could begin again with someone else. . . . May God deliver me from men. But He needn't bother. I know the sin into which I've fallen. It's a shameful thing to bow down before any fallible human creature.

172

Had I only been rational, had I only thought ahead instead of rushing forward and burning my bridges behind me, I would now have a sheet-anchor, a last recourse. But how base it would have been to leave myself a loop-hole! You know, I never understood Tom Thumb. When you have the kind of horrible parents who abandon you in the forest just so they'll have a little more to eat—why, you let yourself die of grief. When your one and only love forsakes you, you kick the bucket too, like the old servant in *The Cherry Orchard*—dismissed and forgotten, a cast-off object, a worn-out thing. Your time is up.

173

In the beginning you loved me in a kind of way. You weren't sure of me then: I might escape you. As for me, I was frightened. I fought hard, realizing I'd have to go on

playing "hard to get," keeping my distance. For you like a
woman to resist you at first.

You gave your wife no pleasure, no fulfilment. You
never saw her dishevelled, panting, in the throes of lust.
So you can be "faithful" to her, in your fashion. It's
amusing to think that, of the two of us, I am the more
"betrayed." You, wretched puritan that you are, could
not forgive me the sensual pleasure we shared.

174

There's no denying it, Pierre. We shared the ultimate
experience of desire. For ten years. Unfailingly. Ten
years with no decrease of impulse or fulfilment, and
against all the odds of time and circumstance. Even that
last time when I knew you would not revoke your "decision." In the midst of my tears and sobs I knew the
supreme pleasure. And you still can't understand. You
fancy some casual lover can satisfy me.

Why should I keep on writing? I'll never succeed in
putting into words what I feel. Throughout that final
embrace I was deciding it would be the last one for me. I
would die rather than play out some wretched parody of
love with someone else.

175

I loved you. I kept on loving you. And I love you still, no
doubt, through this delirium that in some kindly way is
coming over me. . . . The words are blurring, all those
cruel words you uttered for so many years to make me *toe
the line* like some awkward recruit. Oh, if I had only
hidden my passion I would still have you with me.

176

Other passions, madly indulged, lead one to jail. Alas, not this one of mine! People are no longer put in prison for adultery or idolatry. I wish they were. My suffering would be the less, except on visiting days.

177

I would like to recover my voice. To cry out, roll on the floor, dance with rage. To scream at the injustice, the sheer pillage of the self. I'll do nothing of the kind. You did well in picking *me* out. There's no chance of my causing any scandal. No one will notice my disappearance. Only a ripple on the water, a swiftly stifled gasp. And silence.

178

With an effort—the time of my eternal sleep is drawing near!—I can perhaps recover some moments of truth. To begin with, I had some margin of freedom. You managed to give me a few instants of unalloyed happiness by preserving the absolute secrecy to which we both subscribed. Nobody must know. No one was to suffer from our "transgression," as you called it. I found this fair enough. And so there were those perfect moments when we walked together in the sunlight, in the woods, by the seashore. I would perform prodigies to be with you for a few hours. Sometimes for a whole night. Whether in Paris or New York didn't matter. Oh, I have slept with you in so many hotels and motels. Slipping in by the service entrance, stealing like a thief into your room, looking right and left lest I be observed. Hiding in the bathroom when anyone knocked. What did I care? The telephone would ring.

"You know, I'm a man who is always on call."

It was your secretary, or one of your patients. Or your wife. And you would talk to her long and patiently of a hundred things you had in common . . .

At last I'm escaping from this *corrida*.

179

I had to lie like a trooper. You grudged me my "happiness," and made me pay dearly for it. Whenever you had made me wildly happy by swearing, as if unwillingly, that you were in love with me, you would leave me for days and weeks without a word, without even telephoning. I waited. I beat my head against the wall. I would play solitaire: red on black, black on red, over and over. Or I would knit. Dazed. Only the sound of the telephone roused me from my trance. Even here, each ring pierces my eardrums.

180

I have always detested the sham "literature" that sings a paean to female slavery: *Back Street, The Story of O*. Yet I am just as mad as those atrocious masochistic heroines. *Mirror, mirror on the wall, who is for him the fairest one of all?* Lie to me, dear deceitful looking-glass. . . . Hearing your occasional assurances—those few miserable, charitable words wrenched from you—I felt rich and filled with gratitude.

181

I've had enough. Sentence me. To the electric chair, the guillotine, the noose. It doesn't matter. Let's get it over. I refuse to submit to the lie-detector. I'll keep the vilest of my secrets to myself.

182

I spent years of my life pressing my nose against the shop-window of marital bliss. North America flaunts its wealth in these picture-windows peopled by loving couples in lovely suburbs. It's only right that I should bewail my personal counterfeit of that bliss, my own little backyard reverie.

183

I won't go around begging for pity. My heart has undergone a change too. Turned to stone. Hard as yours. . . . Thank Heaven I am in Venice. *La Serenissima.* There are no beggars in Venice. The poorest people have kept their pride. Venice the wholly beautiful, about to sink into her lagoon. It's not so bad, making one's last bow against such a gorgeous background.

184

I'm really in luck. It will be an "easy" death. A death of my own choosing. At my own chosen hour too, without the infirmities of age or the pinch of poverty. For these last two months of my "holidays" I've enjoyed the nice things that money can buy. The fine clean linen, the well-made bed, the well-served meals. Every day, for no reason at all, someone has greeted me kindly. I know none of the frightful anguish of the neurotic, nor the delirium of drugs. No one is hounding me. I am the artisan of my own destruction: the artisan, not the artist! I've nothing to do with art's violence and beauty, only with the web patiently patterned on my suffering through the years. The work of a blind, persistent spider.

185

For years I made myself an automaton, unconsciously grinding wheat and tares alike. Mechanically turning my little word-mill, my prayer-wheel. Like a machine, not thinking what I was saying. How good of these young people, my students, not to denounce me as an impostor! I deserve it. Present in body, absent in spirit. Lost in dreams and expectations.

186

At least I'm spared the beginning of the September term. They'll have no trouble finding somebody else. These long teachers' holidays are some use after all. Examination of the conscience, the vocation. I won't be taking those examinations again. I've opted out.

187

My sense of guilt is increasing. Some faulty reckonings

don't go unpunished. I've been a bad bookkeeper. The balance of my account towards others shows a deficit.

188

The life of work, the life of love. At first I hoped to drive them abreast. But I cheated. I vowed I would never renounce my "ideas," my beliefs. I had taken up again with Thérèse and Marguerite. I joined them in a score of their "causes." I had not their purity of motive. You couldn't bear my "militance," my "wretched feminism." Did I lend my voice to such things only to anger you? You had nothing but contempt for my "soul." You were inwardly convinced I had "lost" it—or perhaps had never had such a thing, as some mediaeval theologians claimed. I return the compliment. You are a money-grubber. You worship power, influence, things you can touch and see. Each beam in your country house, each stone in your town house, are more precious to you than my tears. You are fonder of your possessions than of the memories we share. I always knew it, and you never denied it. Your wife is only another of your chattels, with the diamond on her finger, the mink on her back, and your swarm of brats to complete the picture.

189

Now I'm getting vulgar. I want to avoid these coarse and spiteful thoughts that make me sink into the baseness I detest.

190

With the approach of death I am discovering hatred. At last I dare to hate you. The distance between us is a help. And the closeness of the end. Old rancours are reviving, seeping into my heart, flooding it with disgust. Venice is so beautiful. The façade is intact above the rotten piles. They're said to be in danger of crumbling before the first tidal wave.

191

There are mornings when at high tide the city's refuse comes to the surface. A strange collection of bits and pieces appears on the green water of the canals. Just so, at dawn, my heart is swamped by waves of rage which bring long-buried horrors to light. Horrors so long and so patiently hidden, now performing their *danse macabre*.

192

There was once, for me, the resurrection of the flesh. My body, awkward and unpleasing, so far despised by others and by myself, could be the delight of someone else! A marvellous revelation which reconciled me to the miracle of the Incarnation. You made me "restore all things to their rightful place." And then you crushed me with the weight of your own remorse.

193

For you did feel remorse. We had agreed that "nobody" would have to pay for this "transgression"—whose weight

I alone was to bear! I could never finish enumerating the punishments you devised for me. The nights, suddenly cut short, when you made me get dressed again and run off like a prostitute hired by the hour; your parting words and farewell warnings; your repeated threats to "break off for good and all." I would beg you on my knees, cling to your clothing. People find Madame du Barry ignoble for clinging to the bars of her prison to prevent being dragged to the scaffold: it seems they had to break her fingers before cutting off her head. I understood her. There is no action, however base or cowardly, I would not have performed to defer my own execution. I gave up at last. Life is more cruel and infamous than the blackest stories we can invent. Even here on this page, the only confessional I have, I will not reveal how far my weakness carried me.

194

In our sensual joy I thought I had found the reason for life itself. I was so besotted with the power of love that I myself wished to have a child, to "make life," in the words of my beloved Zola. I felt strong enough to succumb to a love that would bind me forever. I wished to complete and perfect this physical ecstasy by the only "work" that matters to a woman: a child made in the image of the man she loves.

195

You laughed at this "grotesque" fancy of mine. You had always taken the necessary precautions. When I was suffi-ciently broken in and "brought to heel," you left the business to me. Like an honest servant, I didn't cheat. I took my little pill religiously, twenty-one times a month.

196

In the six years of your marriage before I came along, you gave your wife two children. After that, you gave her three more. I was regaled with all the details, the sketches and snapshots, of these lucky heirs of your body. Don't tell me about the pains of childbirth. Or else I'll describe the absurd suffering of aborting, month after month, a small sterile egg.

197

Proust has described to perfection the subtlest nuances of jealousy, where the pain of being deceived is doubled by the agony of uncertainty. Oh, it is more agonizing to *know*, beyond all possible doubt! To endure the long sleepless nights when one knows, without the hope of changing anything, what is going on in the darkness with someone else.

I am amazed that I lasted all those years without going mad from suffering. Yet with Proust, after *le temps perdu* comes—and so beautifully!—*le temps retrouvé*. I am wandering in the maze of my absurd passion where nothing but gall and wormwood is *retrouvé*. If I have endured all these torments, surely it should have been to find some reason for them! "One must think Sisyphus was happy."[6] Well, I'm no longer rolling my stone. I'll never see you again. It's all over. Pierre, I shall die without bidding you goodbye.

198

It's right and fitting that you denied me the happiness of bearing your child. I would be tied to him. And I would hate him to be like you. I would tremble to see myself in him. I would have to live for him. And here I am, free! Free after all those years of slavery. Criminals are no longer punished by solitary confinement. Without clearly knowing why—was it so I could meet you at any time and anywhere?—I abandoned my claim to any settled life with you. You declared that divorce was a dreadful thing. I divorced myself from my own kind, to be with you. In return, you despised me for my blind devotion.

199

So this body of mine, after its little hour of glory, was not allowed to flower into a true woman's body, heavy and rounded, ripening like a melon in the September sun. I've taken good care of it, because its outward show was what you liked: I nearly ruined myself in beauty shops! Love of the body, hatred of the flesh: that was the drink you mixed for me. I tossed it off again and again, till I was drunk. Yes, of course, it's a sin. To keep you, to wrench a few words of tenderness out of you, I was willing to use the most "abandoned" caresses. That was how you described them, attacking my self-respect. Puritan! Pharisee! Never will I go back to your horrible province. All those black cattle, your schoolmasters, taught you nothing. It's not "carnal" love that is beastly, but contempt for another creature.

200

All this summer, the last summer of my life, Venice has lain before me. With its treasures, its dreams. I've been turned in upon myself, painfully leafing through the pages of my past. I've seen nothing here, liked nothing.

The only "world event" that reached me was those few awkward steps taken on the moon. A pair of men, swaddled in immense casings, dancing their strange ballet. Beyond the force of gravity and matter. Released from the earth. So one *can* free oneself, escape into space! Yet I didn't ask you for the moon. Only for a few moments of light. For me, love was the celebration of a change that let me escape from my earthly state, a marvellous ascension where I could at last meet a spiritual presence through the ecstasy of the flesh.

201

In this self-inquisition, everything becomes questionable. I'm no longer sure whether I brought you the same gift. In sensual pleasure too, I was doubtless alone in that flight beyond myself, alone in my ecstasy.

202

Proust is right. Uncertainty is worst of all. If I weren't still hoping for some unthinkable miracle I would kill myself now. I'm waiting, hoping.

203

I'm exhausted. This pain of being forsaken. There are no
further betrayals possible. *Consummatum est.* I'm not
even worth thirty pieces of silver. Peter fell alseep on the
Mount of Olives. You fell asleep in my arms. I cannot
think you will not wake before my last agony. Pierre, for
the love of that God you claim to believe in, do not forsake
me.

204

The sceptic derides the mystic. He claims the mystical
dialogue with God is like that of ordinary lovers. And the
psychiatrists tell us that when nuns are going mad they
mouth obscenities that would make a guardsman blush. I
understand this blend of "tones." If I had to describe our
embraces I would do it in the same way. You used to laugh
at my "litanies," my need to repeat your name over and
over, as if I were giving thanks. You never spoke my
name. I was your "poppet." Your thing, in a word. There's
no use going on. You washed your hands of me. The way
you do after making a sick call. When you left me it was
like the withdrawal of life itself. Every parting was like
some bitter trial imposed on me. A passage from light into
darkness, into the dark night of the soul. I am no longer
afraid of death. I have endured it a thousand times, each
time you left me.

205

There is no end to the heart's desolations. I could never
get used to seeing you go. I hid my distress as well as I

could. I tried not to panic, not to afflict you with "scenes."
You found my ceremonial farewells irksome. You were
looking at the clock.

206

And all the time the trap was closing. I was strictly forbidden to telephone you. "I'll be in touch." Once and once
only I broke the rule. Brutally, you put me in my place.
You would do anything to spare your family the least
disturbance. You made me weep for hours on end, suffering your displeasure. You meant to "punish" me, to teach
me not to "do it again," like a child. Mechanically I'd keep
telling myself, *I am Sophie, facing Madame Fichini.* I've
just remembered the title of the first book I ever read: *Les
Malheurs de Sophie.*[7]

207

I adored those "misfortunes" of Sophie. And I associated ·
them, passionately, with those that you heaped on me.
My love for you was mixed with the pain that gave it its
salt, its savour. "There is no such thing as a happy love." I
used to love those unhappy abortive love affairs in books.
I never had any illusions about my own fate. For me too it
would be the Nazi "final solution." The murderers of the
Gestapo knew all about it. The ones they tortured spoke
up quickly. Or kept silent. It was stupid to undergo
horrible sufferings only to "spill the beans" in the end. All
suffering binds all of us closer together. Never would I
have dared to break this tie. When you gave me my
walking papers—"it's time we called it quits: try and
forget me over the holidays"—I was struck dumb. You

136

had expected me to break out howling. And I, I was suddenly relieved! Like the condemned man who has been thinking that each resounding step outside his cell may announce "the" moment. When at last his body is shaved and "prepared," he suffers less than from the terrible period of waiting. I could have won a reprieve, a remission of my sentence. And for once you left me an address where I could reach you. I won't use it. Never. You're a strange person. Yes, you were disappointed —like a child who has gone to see the fireworks and missed the climax.

208

Sly as the goose about to be eaten by the fox, I'll dress up my suicide. No proof of it will ever come to light. This supreme surrender of mine will have no record in your files. It will only go to prove you were right. "She was unbalanced—a madwoman. A good thing I got rid of her before she made trouble."

209

Sleep well, good people. You need no captain of the watch. The scum of society will have its revenge, in silence.

210

Yet there were moments of such sweetness, of such piercing beauty.

211

The Lord has given everything. The Lord has taken everything away. Blessed be the name of the Lord. I set my face against His law.

212

Those cruel forefathers of mine. I'd like to ascend Mount Sinai and seize the Tables of the Law. And shatter them again. I am prepared to violate the law of life and the law of death. I know what I'm doing. And I claim my privilege with pride.

213

The Lord has given us life. And then death. He gives only to take back. I shun these Indian gifts. I would rather have received nothing at all. I was resigned to my fate. Then He dangled a shining hope before me. Like those worthy souls who at Christmas-time seek out some orphan in a foundling home. They give him a "beautiful" holiday, with gifts and candies, and a seat at the festive family board. And on the morning of New Year's Day they send him back to his icy little dormitory.

214

I feel very "Jewish" today. The God of my mother's people is taking his vengeance. God the Father, who forbade the making of likenesses in His image. Ah, this sketch of mine—of you—would be hardly flattering to the Creator.

215

Perhaps God did create you in his own likeness. Not me. I'm glad to be a woman, a Jewess with neither country, homeland nor property. With nothing. Betrayed. I've nothing left. And I'd like to open my hands, empty my heart of all bitterness and tell you, "Believe me, I don't hate you at all."

216

I'll be a double-goer to the end. A shuffler between love and hate, between the Old Testament and the New. Forswearing both. I don't believe in the Incarnation. Like my ancestors, I think we are awaiting our own Messiah. It was you that I hailed as my saviour. Mary Magdalene was not rejected. But you found my offerings ill-timed. And yet my oils and perfumes rejoiced your heart. I feel I am going mad.

217

There's a very fine little picture in the Museo Correr. A Crucifixion by Bellini, all in a heavenly blue. And the face of Christ is ravaged by sorrow. How delicious to believe in this miracle of a man who suffers for us, with us, and at our hands. Not the Son of God, but an ordinary man.

When I can do nothing more I walk for hours through
Venice. The bells sound from all the campaniles. Like so
many appeals. With never a response. Far from the places
frequented by the tourists—those beautiful classified,
indexed churches—you find the quiet dark ones. It is cool
there, and you can sit down. Silence reigns. Sometimes a
priest is officiating, or a sacristan is sweeping the floor.
And there is always a bent old woman in black, praying.
She performs some small useless tasks, brings a few flowers, weeps. In the house of God, the house of man, you
can always find a woman who has voluntarily become a
servant.

August the fifteenth. The grand festival of the lovely
Italian summer. With its profusion of flowers on the altars. And its wealth of waxen lights. At the entrance of the
Church of the Frari a woman was repeating, "A hundred
lire, only a hundred lire apiece!" I was able to overcome
my disgust. I went in, carrying my unlit candle. At first I
wanted to put it down—somewhere, anywhere. To hide
it. But a candle is meant to burn. I approached the most
deserted altar, and tried to light it from another. As if for
the sacrifice of Cain, the flame would not kindle. The wick
caught at last. I managed to place this candle beside the
others. And I saw I had brought the seventh light to the
candelabrum.

A weak light, shining faintly. If only I could accept this role in your life. A little light that flickers a few seconds, before dying in the loveless dark.

And I loved the light with such passion. You will never know how certain lights in September and February plucked at my heart. I was never at your side in broad daylight, in the blaze of noon on the whiteness of snow or the redness of maples. For us, always and shamefully, the night. This suicide must also take place in the darkness. I wish I could recall that last line of Phèdre's,

To restore to the day its purity . . .[8]

Everything I loved is escaping me. Even those lines of Racine. Loss of the sunlight, of colours, festivals. Women like me are no longer stoned to death. I shan't run through the litanies of their modern avatars. All those female clichés. They're deadly enough in books. In real life, one is just as sick of them.

God was right. Those must be saved who value life enough to flee, following their noses, letting the flames devour the wreckage behind them. Lot and his family. His daughters are young, their life is all before them. But for the old wife, it is her whole past that is being swallowed up. So she turns her head, trying to see what is happening—and what has happened. She looks back, breaking the commandment. Poor old woman. In the Bible you have no name. Lot's wife, that was enough. And you were not to disobey, but to keep walking right on, on the appointed road. To what forgotten sin were you faithful? Why that last glance that nailed you to the ground? A pillar of salt. A fine image, a most telling symbol. A pillar of petrified tears. The tears of old women who can no longer keep up with the others. They look back and mourn. The others don't even notice they're gone: they themselves are moving on. And they will fool your man. And he will see nothing. You, you are turned to a statue. In a happy dream Lot is embracing a young woman, pretty and firm of flesh, feeling neither remorse nor regret. I'll no longer torture myself thinking of my successor, of her youth, her beauty. Only long enough to shed a tear or two, and that is enough.

224

I too am looking back—on this ruined past, this wreckage where nothing survives of all I loved. Everything is abolished and consumed. Who is there to hold me back? Or to drive me on, to call on me for some final effort, some last burst of courage? You've left me in the lurch. Shift for yourself, my dear girl. Go read your fine books. Tell yourself pretty stories. You wouldn't fall into line with the others: *Double-file, and no talking!* You wanted to live the way they do in novels. Now you'll be able to write one. Like the grasshopper, *She danced for but a single summer.*[9]

"Well, go into your dance now." How I hate you for

your cleverness, the answers you have for everything.
Yes, I danced—but on a tightrope and without a net. I'm
not sorry. Those butterflies in my dream, those fragile
butterflies of the fields, they too live for only a day. My
time is up.

225

The Lord has given everything. The Lord has taken everything back. I'll take the Lord's hour by the forelock,
make it my own. Blessed be the name of the Lord who
hath allowed us to choose the hour of our death. I'll slip
away into the darkness. I, so frightened of everything all
my life, I'll go bravely to my death.

226

I still draw back. To survey this past that has escaped me.
And once again I'm a little girl on the day of her confirma-
tion.
    "I renounce the devil and all his works, the vain pomp
and glory of this world, and I bind myself to Jesus Christ
and to his Church, now and forevermore." I trembled as I
spoke the words. And all those voices, bawling out of
tune, joined in with my own: "I bind myself, I bind
myself. . . ."

227

And I bound myself to this love I had for you. Trembling.
Today you can deny it. But then you were by my side.
And we knew what we were doing.

228

There's no end to this talk of Napoleon's bicentenary. Its echoes keep reaching me. People keep on talking about Waterloo. With a bit of luck the defeat might have been a victory. I've gone through my own campaign without ever seeing the sun rise on an Arcola, an Austerlitz. I took my reverses in the darkness. Getting up again after every fall. Like a bad boxer matched with someone beyond his weight. Round after round. He's already beaten, he's on the ropes, he's down. But he won't take a knockout. At the count of nine he gets up.

229

I won't get up. I've had enough. Throw in the towel. I'm not a pretty sight.

230

Yet in the ancient world, in those cruel days of the Roman circus, they saluted those who were about to die for having put up a good fight.

I fought well. In my defeat there was neither mistake nor mischance. I put all I had into the contest. And more. It wouldn't be so bad if I could discover an error, a moment of carelessness. I gave everything I had. And it was not enough. Carefully, deliberately, you weighed me. And found me wanting.

I won't quarrel with the scales. Nor claim the weights were false. Nor revive any memories. O dear discretion of the dumb, I invoke your wisdom.

232

Pierre, my cruel and stony love. I'll not leave you without this last confession. *Death, where is thy victory?* After all these years, at last the frontier is crossed. You meet me half way. No further shameful wall between us, as in Berlin or Jerusalem, those cities cut in half and mourning their vanished unity. You and I, together at last. Pierre and Hélène. Hélène and Pierre. You speak my name, and give me a place in your heart. A place where I can live in the noonday of love. As in that garden or cemetery, I'm not sure which—yes, it's a cemetery, because the living hour is always beating at the door of death—where Ysé meets Mesa.[10] When they see they are linked forever . . . I have had such an hour of revelation. Outwardly nothing was changed. We were only more prudent, more often apart. It made no difference. The waiting was a small matter—only from one moment of happiness to another. That was the price I had to pay. I paid it without complaining. Jacob waited seven years for Rachel. And when the seven years were up he sought her from her father, who laid seven more years of waiting on him. I no longer have such courage. . . . How brief it was, my little span of happiness. In those last months there were times when I slept beside you. I had never done so before. I dared not waste a moment. I listened to your breathing. I spent those hours fixing your features in my mind. I was never sure of seeing you again. At least I knew the ecstasy of sleeping quietly and without fear in your arms. Safe. Sheltered. At peace.

233

The horrible awakening. The lion-tamer in the cage can never let his gaze shift for an instant. Like a tiger making his lightning attack, you charged. For the first time I was disarmed, caught off balance, in all the nakedness of my foolish trust. You destroyed everything.

234

You too were afraid of being trapped by love. I should forgive you. You too were fighting for your freedom —fiercely, deaf and blind to anything else, like a wild beast. And you spoke out. Horrible words.

235

It's more than twenty years since my parents died. I can still hear their voices, see their faces. I've forgotten the very tone of your voice. I wouldn't recognize you in the street.

236

Once only my hands were full. I had to open them. To let you escape. And I would like to clasp them, as if in some moment of love, some moment when your hand held

mine. To ask God's mercy on you and on myself. On "us."
Forgive them, for they know not what they do.

237

In lands the locust haunts at noon . . . [11] I'm forgetting all
the poems I loved. I can remember only that *Cimetière
marin,* [12] which I no longer need since I've no desire to
"try to live," only to die.

And I went in the full blaze of noon to San Michele.
And the cicada's cry was as piercing as in the heat of
Greece. Not a cloud in this sky *of a blue so blue*—in the
words of that silly song we loved. And the thousands of
white crosses, all alike, recording the slaughter of soldiers
in war. And walking on the marble pavement that bears
the tombs of the wealthy Venetian families, you feel the
commingling of death, earth, sea and sun. A few cypres-
ses cast their shade. On the tombstones are hideous votive lights, photographs in metal frames, withered flowers,
absurd plastic posies, inscriptions touching and romantic.
And always, as in the churches, a woman at each turning
of the paths, moving with little steps, hoeing weeds,
planting, raking. Death's little housewiferies. There are
the cats too. Not the lordly Venetian cats lounging in
splendour on the city squares, but small, thin, very young
ones, slinking furtively among the tombstones. People
who can't bear to drown a litter of kittens leave them here
quietly. And certain old women—always the same
ones—come here every day to bring them scraps, offal,
fish-heads. I found a little plot of greenery facing the sea,
choked with wild grass, a kind of *Paradou* [13] gone to seed.
Almost gone back to a wild state. Not a single cross. A few
neglected headstones with half-effaced inscriptions in

many languages. The Strangers' Corner, for foreigners struck down by death in Venice. It was very cool there, facing the sea. It will be good to sleep here, in this place reserved for the outcasts of religion and love.

238

Hope keeps playing its wretched tricks to the very end. On my way out of the hotel I was handed a letter from Canada. My heart stopped beating. It was my income tax receipt. So, I've settled accounts with the State.

239

And I've settled up here too. I've just paid my hotel bill. My bags are packed. Everything is in order. I have everything planned. First the *vaporetto* to the Lido. Then the little café. A mineral water to wash down my pills, one by one. The short walk to that corner of the beach which is always deserted. Under my dress, my bathing-suit. The water is mild at this time of year, even at ten o'clock at night. Quietly take one stroke, then another, towards the open sea. Without turning back. And the pills are beginning to work. The sea is soft and salty—it bears me up—and now I'm floating—adrift off to sleep. And the waves cradle and cover me. I've only to sink into silence.

240

"Enough of your blab!"[14] Zazie's phrase recalls me to my task, and none too soon either. "You're dreaming, baby. Go ahead and dive, without all this horsing around."

One likes to polish one's final phrase. Then cast one's bottle of spleen on the waters. These poor pages, the mocking proof that in the long run everything is "literature." Life, love, death. Their portrait and parody. Only a pastime to make us forget the death of passion. The idea of suicide slips away like the lover of a night. *Patience, and shuffle the cards*. Life resumes its hold on the victim of life. I'll go on living.

NOTES

1. V. Racine, *Bérénice*, IV, 5.

2. *J'ai deux amours (mon pays et Paris)*, popular song of the 1920's.

3. By Georges Bernanos (1949).

4. By François Mauriac (1927).

5. V. Boileau, *L'Art Poétique*.

6. V. *Le mythe de Sisyphe*, by Albert Camus (1942).

7. By the Comtesse de Ségur (1854).

8. Cf. Racine, *Phèdre*, V, 7.

9. *Elle n'a dansé qu'un seul été*, title of a film directed by Arne Mattson (1951).

10. V. *Partage de midi*, by Paul Claudel (1906).

11. V. *Anabase*, by St-John Perse (1924).

12. By Paul Valéry (1926).

13. The luxuriant wilderness in Zola's *La Faute de l'Abbe Mouret* (1875).

14. V. *Zazie dans le Métro*, by Raymond Queneau (1959).